Table of Contents

Introduction

The HELP concept began approximately ten years ago in our attempt as practicing speech-language pathologists to organize our stacks of handwritten therapy exercises into a format that could be used more efficiently with our clients and their families. What evolved from this early attempt at organization has far exceeded our most grandiose expectations. We found that other language instructors, like us, were in great need of therapy materials which were concise, yet provided numerous practice activities across a variety of language areas.

The philosophy underlying HELP 1 and 2 has motivated and influenced the development of HELP 3. In this workbook, we have attempted to present tasks related to daily activities and experiences in a format that can be used easily by clients, as well as their clinicians, teachers, family members, paraprofessionals and others working to improve communication skills. Careful attention has been given to the focus and scope of the tasks to ensure that the items presented reflect the interests and practical concerns of clients of a variety of ages and ability levels.

IEP goals have been included to further explain the individual tasks and to help the instructor write goals. The general activities sections also assist in the carryover of skills learned within the sections to everyday situations.

The following guidelines are offered for effective utilization of the tasks in HELP.

1. Many tasks are presented as written worksheets for the client. Use your own judgment in presenting the tasks orally or as worksheets, depending on the ability of your client and your overall purpose for specific remediation.

2. As the ages and skills of the children or adults will vary, use your own judgment as to which portions of each section to use for your clients. Items within each task have been arranged, when possible, from the easier items to the more difficult.

3. Common, correct responses have been provided for almost all items in the answer key. There may, however, be other acceptable answers, depending on the client's experiences and cultural background. Again, use your discretion in determining correctness of responses.

4. Many repetitions of items may be necessary before target accuracy levels are reached. Keep track of the client's performance on the specific items chosen to be within his ability range.

5. Strive to achieve carryover of target areas in conversation, everyday and classroom activities through constant repetition, questioning and stressing of specific concepts. These exercises may be used by parents and teachers' aides successfully with little explanation from the instructor. Communication between home and school is essential if carryover is to be effective. Carryover is essential to derive the maximum benefit from therapy.

We cannot offer this addition to the HELP series without extending our appreciation to our many colleagues whose support has been instrumental in the success of HELP. Your positive comments and suggestions have been a source of encouragement to us in developing HELP 3. As you add HELP 3 to your professional libraries, we hope you will continue to find the HELP series to be of practical value in your remediation efforts with language-impaired individuals.

AML
PMP

Concepts

Knowledge of basic concepts is the cornerstone of the intricate building known as the human language system. Without these building blocks of information, learning and experimentation with the environment cannot occur. Only after principle concepts have been acquired can verbal expression arise and meaningful communication result.

Within this section, various tasks are presented to enable the client to discern as well as to describe the relationships between individuals, time, places, things, events and situations. The material progresses from easier to more difficult concepts, incorporating simple to more complex tasks. Skillful use of this section will allow the client to discover and assimilate information about his environment.

Task A: Telling Where Items Are Found

Name the place or container where you usually find these things. The first one is done for you.

1. towels, soap, toilet paper, toothpaste, shampoo   *bathroom*

2. pots and pans, toaster, silverware, microwave oven, blender   _____

3. wallet, lipstick, checkbook, tissue, brush   _____

4. shoes, shirts, pants, sweaters, jackets   _____

5. dolls, puzzles, balls, trucks, blocks   _____

6. socks, underwear, shorts, T-shirts, sweaters   _____

7. thermos, sandwich, napkin, cookies, chips   _____

8. jackets, boots, coats, umbrella, hat   _____

9. milk, eggs, cheese, butter, lettuce   _____

10. rooms, attic, basement, windows, doors   _____

11. soap powder, bleach, fabric softener, pre-wash spray, hangers   _____

12. knives, forks, spatula, measuring spoons, vegetable peeler   _____

13. screwdrivers, nails, hammer, screws, wrench   _____

14. pencils, ruler, pens, envelopes, paper clips   _____

15. swing set, sandbox, merry-go-round, picnic tables, trees   _____

16. needle, thread, scissors, buttons, snaps   _____

17. sugar, salt, flour, vinegar, tea   _____

18. towels, sheets, pillow cases, washcloths, tablecloths   _____

19. spare tire, jack, jumper cables, rope, flashlight   _____

20. crib, changing table, diapers, stuffed toys, baby blanket   _____

21. water bowl, bone, bed, dog food, chain   _____

I.E.P. Goal: When presented with a list of common items, the client will identify the places the items are ususally found, with 90% or greater accuracy.

Task A: Telling Where Items Are Found, *continued*

Name the place or container where you usually find these things.

22. thermometer, aspirin, Band-Aids, antiseptic cream, cough syrup   _____

23. gym suit, sneakers, towel, socks, deodorant   _____

24. paprika, pepper, parsley, oregano, thyme   _____

25. money, driver's license, photographs, I.D. card, social security card   _____

26. keys, change, wallet, handkerchief, comb   _____

27. bottles, diapers, rattle, blanket, teething ring   _____

28. files, reports, pens, calendar, calculator   _____

29. tongue depressor, stethoscope, thermometer, bandages, syringes   _____

30. pews, hymnals, Bibles, pulpit, altar   _____

31. sunglasses, towel, suntan lotion, portable radio, hat   _____

32. snakebite kit, pocketknife, water bottle, compass, snacks   _____

33. books, card catalogs, encyclopedias, carrels, stacks   _____

34. desk, telephone, secretary, appointment book, files, payroll   _____

35. stores, fountains, escalators, restaurants, specialty shops   _____

36. jets, security gates, baggage claim area, gas trucks, runways   _____

37. pages, index, appendices, bibliography, title page   _____

38. swing, folding chairs, doormat, railing, steps   _____

39. rake, lawn mower, shovel, fertilizer, wheelbarrow   _____

40. basketball hoops, parallel bars, bleachers, sports equipment, mats   _____

41. memos, dividers, file folders, correspondence, reports   _____

42. bonds, insurance papers, coins, will, jewelry   _____

I.E.P. Goal: When presented with a list of common items, the client will identify the places the items are usually found, with 90% or greater accuracy.

Task B: Identifying Spatial Relationships

Choose the correct answer for each question. The first one is done for you.

1. Do you find pictures on the wall or under the wall?   <u>on</u>   under

2. Do you put dog food in a bowl or on a bowl?   in   on

3. At a meeting, do people sit beside each other or below each other?   beside   below

4. Do you put money under a bank or in a bank?   under   in

5. When you stand in line, is the first person in front of you or behind you?   in front of   behind

6. Do you use an umbrella on your head or over your head?   on   over

7. Do fish swim on the water or in the water?   on   in

8. Do people look through a window or around a window?   through   around

9. Do you look through a mirror or at a mirror?   through   at

10. If someone is last in line, does he stand after or before you?   after   before

11. Do you cook on an oven or in an oven?   on   in

12. Are oak trees planted inside or outside a house?   inside   outside

13. Does flour go into or across cookie batter?   into   across

14. Do you fill a glass up or down?   up   down

15. Do you put toast on or in a toaster?   on   in

16. Do you sit beside or behind your date in a theater?   beside   behind

17. Do you sit on a booth or in a booth?   on   in

18. When using a VCR, do you record a TV show on tape or in tape?   on   in

19. Do you wear a coat under or over your clothes?   under   over

20. Are headlights located on the front or on the back of a car?   on the front   on the back

I.E.P. Goal: Given a choice of response, the client will answer questions concerning spatial relationships, with 90% or greater accuracy.

Task B: Identifying Spatial Relationships, *continued*

Choose the correct answer for each question.

21. Do you go over or through a doorway?	over	through
22. Are cleansers kept in the sink or under the sink?	in	under
23. Do you eat under or at a table?	under	at
24. Do you meet friends at or on a restaurant?	at	on
25. Does water go up or down a drain?	up	down
26. Does smoke go up or down the chimney?	up	down
27. When you go to see a movie, do you go to or from a movie theater?	to	from
28. Should you lean up against or away from a freshly painted wall?	up against	away from
29. Do you drive through a tunnel or under a tunnel?	through	under
30. Do you hang lights on or off a Christmas tree?	on	off
31. Do planes fly under or over buildings?	under	over
32. To fill a glass with milk, do you pour the milk in or out of a milk carton?	in	out of
33. To drive a car, do you get in or out of the car?	in	out of
34. Do books go below or on a bookshelf?	below	on
35. Do trains go beside or across a bridge?	beside	across
36. When you tell someone a secret, should you stand close to or away from him?	close to	away from
37. Do you walk over or under a threshold?	over	under
38. Do you thumb through or over a book?	through	over
39. Should you walk toward or away from an explosion?	toward	away from
40. Do candidates linger among or against their supporters?	among	against

I.E.P. Goal: Given a choice of response, the client will answer questions concerning spatial relationships, with 90% or greater accuracy.

Task C: Correcting Spatial Relationship Statements

Identify the incorrect word in each sentence. Then, restate the sentence using the correct word. The first one is done for you.

1. I wear shoes <u>under</u> my feet.

   I wear shoes on my feet.

2. Albert's hat fell through his head.

   _____

3. Don's glasses slipped up his nose.

   _____

4. The frog jumped between the log.

   _____

5. The car sped around the road.

   _____

6. The raindrops splashed in the porch roof.

   _____

7. I fixed my window screen so the bugs would stay inside.

   _____

8. They laid the new carpet in the living room floor.

   _____

9. Mother asked Beth to sit beside her under the couch.

   _____

10. I tried to put my slacks on the dresser drawer, but it was full.

    _____

11. I couldn't see the movie because the girl behind me was too tall.

    _____

12. Jane warned Larry not to bump his head on the lamp hanging just below his head.

    _____

I.E.P. Goal: The client will identify and correct inappropriate spatial relationship words in statements, with 90% or greater accuracy.

Task C: Correcting Spatial Relationship Statements, *continued*

Identify the incorrect word in each sentence. Then, restate the sentence using the correct word.

13. Lisa went riding in a horse.

_____

14. Jeffrey jumped under a small bush.

_____

15. Someone cut below me when I was waiting in line.

_____

16. The lid was on the bottom of the jar.

_____

17. A table of contents is found outside the book.

_____

18. The helicopter hovered below the football field.

_____

19. The waiter put Michael's dessert behind him on the table.

_____

20. In our house, the basement is just above the kitchen.

_____

21. Jim loves to sleep outdoors over the stars.

_____

22. Josh blew out all the candles in his birthday cake.

_____

23. The last person in line was in front of me.

_____

24. Grandma asked me to stand away from my cousin so she could see who was taller.

_____

25. Bud's cafe has the best chili between town.

_____

I.E.P. Goal: The client will identify and correct inappropriate spatial relationship words in statements, with 90% or greater accuracy.

Task D: Generating Spatial Relationships

Answer these questions using a prepositional phrase. The first one is done for you.

1. Where do you put a record?   <u>on the stereo</u>

2. Where do you wear a belt?   _____

3. Where does a barrette go?   _____

4. Where do ships sail?   _____

5. Where do you wear a watch?   _____

6. Where does a light bulb go?   _____

7. Where is a caboose found?   _____

8. Where does a mole live?   _____

9. Where is a prisoner kept?   _____

10. Where does a helicopter land?   _____

11. Where is a football kicked to score a field goal?   _____

12. When you play leapfrog, where do you jump?   _____

13. Where is a letter mailed?   _____

14. Where do you go swimming?   _____

15. Where does a tunnel go?   _____

16. Where do you wear gloves?   _____

17. Where do we keep coins?   _____

18. When you make a sandwich, where does the ham and cheese go?   _____

19. Where do we wear a scarf?   _____

20. Where do you put your head when you sleep?   _____

I.E.P. Goal: The client will use prepositional phrases to answer spatial relationship questions, with 90% or greater accuracy.

Task D: Generating Spatial Relationships, *continued*

Answer these questions using a prepositional phrase.

21. When you brush your teeth, where does the toothpaste go? _____

22. When you play darts, where should you aim? _____

23. Where should you stand to look in a mirror? _____

24. Where is dental floss used? _____

25. Where do you insert a car key? _____

26. Where does a pitcher throw a baseball? _____

27. Where should you park your car? _____

28. Where is a sling tied? _____

29. When you salute the flag, where should you face? _____

30. Where do we put thread when we sew? _____

31. Where is a mantle? _____

32. Where do we put wrapping paper when we wrap a present? _____

33. Where does a bridge go? _____

34. Where do ocean waves crash? _____

35. Where does marinade go when we marinate meat? _____

36. Where does an athlete run in a race? _____

37. Where does the United States President live? _____

38. Where do people get loans? _____

39. Where is a suburb? _____

40. Where does a ladder lean? _____

I.E.P. Goal: The client will use prepositional phrases to answer spatial relationship questions, with 90% or greater accuracy.

Task E: Part/Whole Relationships — Recipes

Name the food made from each list of ingredients. The first one is done for you.

1. root beer, ice cream _____ ice cream float _____

2. peanut butter, jelly, bread _____

3. chocolate syrup, milk _____

4. cabbage, salad dressing _____

5. lettuce, tomatoes, carrots, celery, cucumbers _____

6. lemons, sugar, water, ice _____

7. sugar, cinnamon, bread, butter _____

8. tuna fish, mayonnaise, bread _____

9. ice cream, milk, strawberries _____

10. dough, tomato sauce, cheese, pepperoni _____

11. grapes, oranges, bananas, cherries, pineapple _____

12. bacon, lettuce, tomato, mayonnaise, bread _____

13. peanuts, oil, sugar _____

14. oil, vinegar, spices _____

15. dried onion soup mix, sour cream _____

16. ground beef, bun, lettuce, tomato, cheese _____

I.E.P. Goal: When presented with a list of ingredients, the client will identify the food made from these ingredients, with 90% or greater accuracy.

Task E: Part/Whole Relationships — **Recipes**, *continued*

Name the food made from each list of ingredients.

17. ham, salami, cheese, lettuce,
    tomato, French bread _____

18. flour, yeast, salt,
    milk, shortening _____

19. potatoes, celery, boiled eggs,
    mayonnaise, mustard _____

20. graham crackers, marshmallows,
    chocolate bar _____

21. potatoes, oil, salt _____

22. crust, apples, cinnamon,
    sugar, butter _____

23. flour, butter, sugar, eggs,
    baking powder, milk _____

24. beef, carrots, onions,
    potatoes, gravy _____

25. chicken, water, onions, salt,
    pepper, noodles _____

26. fruit, sugar, pectin _____

27. kidney beans, onions, tomatoes,
    ground beef, tomato sauce _____

28. ketchup, horseradish _____

29. ground beef, tomato paste,
    hamburger buns, seasons _____

30. corn, lima beans _____

I.E.P. Goal: When presented with a list of ingredients, the client will identify the food made from these ingredients, with 90% or greater accuracy.

Task F: Identifying Activities from Items Used

Name the activity you would do using the items below. The first one is done for you.

1. store, pants, money, cash register, receipt   _buy a pair of pants_

2. dust cloth, vacuum cleaner, mop, bucket, cleansers   _____

3. tub, water, pet shampoo, towel, dog   _____

4. hats, cake, ice cream, presents, games   _____

5. telephone, coins, calling card, phone number, area code   _____

6. letter, return address, envelope, stamp, mailbox   _____

7. picture, hanging wire, hook, nail, hammer   _____

8. camera, film, flash attachment, zoom lens, a subject   _____

9. dirty clothes, detergent, washing machine, fabric softener, water   _____

10. frying pan, chicken, flour, oil, stove   _____

11. helmet, cleats, shoulder pads, football, field   _____

12. shopping cart, grocery list, checkbook, coupons, food   _____

13. marching bands, floats, clowns, balloons, baton twirlers   _____

14. pattern, needles, thread, sewing machine, scissors   _____

15. kindling, newspaper, logs, grate, matches   _____

I.E.P. Goal: The client will identify the activity performed when using a list of items, with 90% or greater accuracy.

Task F: Identifying Activities from Items Used, *continued*

Name the activity you would do using the items below.

16. bathing suit, suntan lotion, towel, hat, sunglasses _____

17. boat, skis, tow rope, life jacket, bathing suit _____

18. ice cream, bananas, chocolate sauce, whipped cream, nuts _____

19. lipstick, mascara, eye shadow, blusher, foundation _____

20. examination, prescription, lenses, frames, mirror _____

21. automobiles, down payment, loan, trade-in, sticker price _____

22. tiller, seed, fertilizer, water, dirt _____

23. topic, reference books, notecards, typewriter, outline _____

24. blood test, license, witness, rings, ceremony _____

25. baggage, motel, maps, free time, tickets _____

26. check, deposit slip, endorsement, bank, teller window _____

27. application, resume, interview, position description, salary requirements _____

28. 1040 forms, W-2 form, calculator, receipts, instructions _____

29. loan, contract, down payment, title search, survey _____

30. candidates, ballots, platform, polls, financial supporters _____

I.E.P. Goal: The client will identify the activity performed when using a list of items, with 90% or greater accuracy.

Task G: Identifying Appropriate Descriptive Words

For each word on the left, choose the appropriate descriptive word or words on the right. The first one is done for you.

1. log	soft	<u>brown</u>	<u>rough</u>
2. socks	stretchy	wooly	sour
3. kitten	huge	cute	rough
4. ice skates	sharp	sturdy	fragile
5. pencil	light	long	pointed
6. ice	cold	warm	hard
7. camera	fragile	portable	buoyant
8. pudding	hard	grainy	gooey
9. flame	bright	luminous	hot
10. scissors	handy	crooked	sharp
11. potato	bumpy	delicate	nutritious
12. servant	helpful	wealthy	obedient
13. hinge	weak	jointed	immobile
14. furniture	useful	decorative	expensive
15. concrete	uncertain	solid	firm
16. carnival	festive	serious	somber
17. egg	oval	round	angular
18. panda	large	furry	guilty

I.E.P. Goal: When presented with groups of adjectives, the client will identify those which describe common items, with 90% or greater accuracy.

Task G: Identifying Appropriate Descriptive Words, *continued*

For each word on the left, choose the appropriate descriptive word or words on the right.

19. hoop	rectangular	triangular	circular
20. shovel	handy	functional	fragile
21. savage	tame	polished	uncivilized
22. locomotive	rapid	noisy	streamlined
23. bathrobe	formal	comfortable	soft
24. judge	learned	impartial	pliable
25. clouds	fluffy	airy	angular
26. nurse	trained	caring	immature
27. gasoline	liquid	soothing	flammable
28. calendar	helpful	sequential	dubious
29. party	festive	fun	instructive
30. dictionary	organized	lengthy	chilling
31. tiger	predictable	feline	fierce
32. bonus	extra	rewarding	confusing
33. jigsaw	challenging	irregular	concave
34. novel	concise	lengthy	intriguing
35. mime	noisy	silent	mute
36. beach	sandy	strident	square

I.E.P. Goal: When presented with groups of adjectives, the client will identify those which describe common items, with 90% or greater accuracy.

Task H: Describing Common Items

Tell at least three things about each item below. Think about what it does, what it
looks like, what parts it has, and what you do with it. The first one is done for you.

1. ball _It's round. You throw it or catch it._
   It comes in different sizes.

2. car _____

   _____

3. sandbox _____

   _____

4. lamp _____

   _____

5. doll _____

   _____

6. door _____

   _____

7. dog _____

   _____

8. house _____

   _____

9. tree _____

   _____

10. book _____

   _____

11. bed _____

   _____

12. telephone _____

   _____

*I.E.P. Goal: When presented with items or events, the client will list their attributes, parts or functions using three
descriptors, with 90% or greater accuracy.*

Task H: Describing Common Items, *continued*

Tell at least three things about each item below. Think about what it does, what it looks like, what parts is has, and what you do with it.

13. backpack _____

_____

14. train _____

_____

15. razor _____

_____

16. drain _____

_____

17. candle _____

_____

18. fan _____

_____

19. placemat _____

_____

20. friend _____

_____

21. parade _____

_____

22. vacation _____

_____

23. swimming pool _____

_____

24. mountain _____

_____

I.E.P. Goal: When presented with items or events, the client will list their attributes, parts or functions using three descriptors, with 90% or greater accuracy.

Task H: Describing Common Items, *continued*

Tell at least three things about each item below. Think about what it does, what it looks like, what parts it has, and what you do with it.

25. deodorant _____

_____

26. highway _____

_____

27. orchard _____

_____

28. wedding _____

_____

29. funeral _____

_____

30. checking account _____

_____

31. schedule _____

_____

32. surgery _____

_____

33. computer _____

_____

34. trial _____

_____

35. Olympics _____

_____

36. election _____

_____

I.E.P. Goal: When presented with items or events, the client will list their attributes, parts or functions using three descriptors, with 90% or greater accuracy.

Task H: Describing Common Items, *continued*

Tell at least three things about each item below. Think about what it does, what it looks like, what parts it has, and what you do with it.

37. circus _____

_____

38. church _____

_____

39. graduation _____

_____

40. soap opera _____

_____

41. helmet _____

_____

42. magazine _____

_____

43. catalog _____

_____

44. meeting _____

_____

45. novel _____

_____

46. real estate _____

_____

47. health insurance _____

_____

48. precipitation _____

_____

I.E.P. Goal: When presented with items or events, the client will list their attributes, parts or functions using three descriptors, with 90% or greater accuracy.

Task I: Answering Relational Questions — One Variable

Answer yes or no to these questions. The first one is done for you.

1. Do you spread jam on bread?	<u>yes</u>	no
2. Can you sit beside yourself?	yes	no
3. Are words printed in a page?	yes	no
4. Can a girl be taller than her brother?	yes	no
5. Can a boat sail behind a lake?	yes	no
6. Are your feet below your knees?	yes	no
7. Does a rug lie on the floor?	yes	no
8. Can you wear a ring on your finger?	yes	no
9. Can everyone be first in line?	yes	no
10. Can you ride a bicycle through a puddle?	yes	no
11. Can children be older than their parents?	yes	no
12. Does the sun pass over the treetops?	yes	no
13. Do you live beside your next-door neighbors?	yes	no
14. Can you hide in front of the door?	yes	no
15. Do you wear a watch around your wrist?	yes	no
16. Do you wear shoes through your feet?	yes	no
17. Can you fold your hands behind your back?	yes	no
18. If you sit down, is the chair beneath you?	yes	no
19. Are your shoulders above your hips?	yes	no
20. Are your lips inside your mouth?	yes	no
21. Does a race car go around a track?	yes	no
22. After you dive into a pool, is there water above you?	yes	no
23. Do you stand inside a mirror to comb your hair?	yes	no
24. Can a truck drive under an overpass?	yes	no
25. Do you wear suspenders below your knees?	yes	no

I.E.P. Goal: When presented with relational questions containing one variable, the client will answer yes or no, with 90% or greater accuracy.

Task J: Making Relational Choices

Tell which of the following you would rather have and why. Underline your choice. The first one is done for you.

1. A few doughnuts or a dozen doughnuts?

   <u>A dozen donuts - I'd have plenty to share.</u>

2. A *C* on a paper or an *F* on a paper?

   _____

3. A batch of cookies or several cookies?

   _____

4. A slice of cake or a sliver of cake?

   _____

5. A stack of change or a stack of bills?

   _____

6. An ounce of gold or a pound of gold?

   _____

7. A deep cut or a surface cut?

   _____

8. A snow flurry or a blizzard?

   _____

9. A downpour of rain or a drizzle?

   _____

10. A series of colds or a single cold?

    _____

11. A dry spell or a drought?

    _____

12. A breeze or a gale?

    _____

I.E.P. Goal: When presented with choices of varying quantity, extent, or degree, the client will explain why one item is preferable, with 90% or greater accuracy.

Task J: Making Relational Choices, *continued*

Tell which of the following you would rather have and why.

13. A difficulty or a disaster?

_____

14. A quart of lemonade or a sip of lemonade?

_____

15. A tank of gas or a gallon of gas?

_____

16. A dish of ice cream or a gallon of ice cream?

_____

17. A pat on the back or a slap on the back?

_____

18. A wait of an eternity or an hour?

_____

19. A couple of flowers or a bouquet?

_____

20. A swarm of mosquitoes or one mosquito?

_____

21. A sprained ankle or a broken one?

_____

22. A pack of chewing gum or a stick of gum?

_____

23. A body temperature of 98° or 103°?

_____

24. A 40% discount or a 15% discount?

_____

I.E.P. Goal: When presented with choices of varying quantity, extent, or degree, the client will explain why one item is preferable, with 90% or greater accuracy.

Task K: Comparing Daily Events — Temporal Relationships

Choose the correct answer to each question. The first one is done for you.

1. Do you eat breakfast before or after lunch?   <u>before</u>   after

2. Is a dryer used first or last when cleaning clothes?   first   last

3. Is medicine taken during or after an illness?   during   after

4. Is the final ingredient in a recipe the first one or the last one to be added?   first   last

5. Do you salute the flag during or following the *Pledge of Allegiance*?   during   following

6. Does Saturday come before or after Friday?   before   after

7. Does intermission happen in the middle or at the end of a show?   in the middle   at the end

8. Do you sign a thank-you note at the beginning or at the end of the note?   at the beginning   at the end

9. Do we eat breakfast in the afternoon or the morning?   afternoon   morning

10. If the doctor wants to see you immediately, should you go to his office right now or wait until next week?   right now   next week

11. Does noon come before or after 11:30 A.M.?   before   after

12. Do you get a marriage license before or after the wedding?   before   after

13. Is furniture delivered before or after it is purchased?   before   after

14. Do you rake the lawn before or after leaves fall?   before   after

15. Is a premature baby born before or after the mother's due date?   before   after

I.E.P. Goal: Given a choice of two responses, the client will answer questions concerning temporal relationships, with 90% or greater accuracy.

Concepts

Task K: Comparing Daily Events — Temporal Relationships, *continued*

Choose the correct answer to each question.

16. Does Sunday immediately follow or precede Saturday? — follow — precede

17. Do promotions occur during or prior to employment? — during — prior

18. If today is Thursday, then is Friday yesterday or tomorrow? — yesterday — tomorrow

19. Does 3 P.M. occur in the afternoon or the morning? — afternoon — morning

20. Does evening precede or follow dusk? — precede — follow

21. Do you make dinner reservations before or after you arrive at the restaurant? — before — after

22. When serving dinner, is the appetizer served first or last? — first — last

23. Are dinner parties held at dawn or at night? — dawn — night

24. Are bathtubs drained following or prior to taking a bath? — following — prior to

25. Are employees paid for hours to come or already worked? — to come — already

26. During a calendar year, does Labor Day always follow or precede Thanksgiving? — follow — precede

27. If something happened in the distant past, did it occur a little while ago or a long time ago? — little while ago — long time ago

28. If the train arrives presently, will it be here in a short time or is it delayed? — in a short time — delayed

29. If two shows are scheduled concurrently, are they playing at the same time or one right after the other? — at the same time — one right after the other

30. If two performers are singing at the same time, are they singing alternately or simultaneously? — alternately — simultaneously

I.E.P. Goal: Given a choice of two responses, the client will answer questions concerning temporal relationships, with 90% or greater accuracy.

Copyright © 1988 LinguiSystems, Inc.

Task L: Comparing Situations and Events

Choose the correct answer for each question. The first one is done for you.

1. Which is longer, a TV commercial or a movie?

   TV commercial   (movie)

2. Which is more scary, riding a roller coaster or riding a merry-go-round?

   roller coaster   merry-go-round

3. Which is sadder, a funeral or a wedding?

   funeral   wedding

4. Which is more dangerous, tennis or hockey?

   tennis   hockey

5. Which is more complicated, buying a new car or buying a new stereo?

   car   stereo

6. Which is more fun, taking an examination or taking a vacation?

   examination   vacation

7. Which is more appealing, going to a surgeon or going to a beautician?

   surgeon   beautician

8. Which is quicker, playing a round of golf or playing a game of racquetball?

   round of golf   game of racquetball

9. Which requires more concentration, playing chess or playing checkers?

   chess   checkers

10. Which takes less time, moving across town or moving to another city?

    across town   to another city

11. Which is more costly to repair, a broken lamp or a broken air conditioner?

    lamp   air conditioner

12. Which requires better speaking skills, a debate or a track meet?

    debate   track meet

I.E.P. Goal: The client will answer questions comparing situations or events, with 90% or greater accuracy.

Task L: Comparing Situations and Events, *continued*

Choose the correct answer for each question.

13. Which requires more strength, playing tennis or Ping-Pong?

        tennis   Ping-Pong

14. Which is more thrilling, riding in a car or riding on a motorcycle?

        in a car   on a motorcycle

15. Which is more educational, visiting a museum or visiting an arcade?

        museum   arcade

16. Which takes more planning, going to church or going on a picnic?

        to church   on a picnic

17. Which is more of an honor, joining a club or being elected to an office?

        joining a club   being elected to an office

18. Which occasion is more joyful, a christening or a sentencing?

        christening   sentencing

19. Which is more relaxing, taking a cold shower or a hot bath?

        cold shower   hot bath

20. Which is more likely to draw a large crowd, a free concert or a city council meeting?

        free concert   city council meeting

21. Which activity burns up more calories, running track or practicing the guitar?

        running track   practicing the guitar

22. Which requires more cooperation, playing backgammon or solitaire?

        backgammon   solitaire

23. Which is more nerve-wracking, watching a comedian or a gymnast?

        comedian   gymnast

24. Which is healthier, eating yogurt or a chocolate nut sundae?

        yogurt   chocolate nut sundae

I.E.P. Goal: The client will answer questions comparing situations or events, with 90% or greater accuracy.

Task L: Comparing Situations and Events, *continued*

Choose the correct answer for each question.

25. Which would invoke a harsher penalty, an overdue library book or an expired driver's license?

      overdue library book   expired driver's license

26. Which gives more independence, driving a car or riding a bus?

      driving a car   riding a bus

27. Which can have more serious consequences, pneumonia or a cold?

      pneumonia   a cold

28. Which requires more patience, teaching a child to swim or to put his socks on?

      to swim   to put his socks on

29. Which event is more sedate, a drag race or a symphony?

      a drag race   a symphony

30. Which is more exhilarating, climbing a mountain or listening to a lecture?

      climbing a mountain   listening to a lecture

31. Which is more depressing, viewing a sunset or witnessing an accident?

      viewing a sunset   witnessing an accident

32. Which is more serious, committing a felony or a misdemeanor?

      felony   misdemeanor

33. Which event is more patriotic, a football game or a presidential inauguration?

      football game   presidential inauguration

34. Which is more likely to happen, being struck by lightning or breaking one's leg?

      being struck by lightning   breaking one's leg

35. Which is more infuriating, getting a promotion or a flat tire?

      promotion   flat tire

36. Which requires more agility, jumping hurdles or hiking?

      jumping hurdles   hiking

I.E.P. Goal: The client will answer questions comparing situations or events, with 90% or greater accuracy.

Concepts

Task M: Arranging Descriptive Words in Order

Put these words in relative order. The first one is done for you.

1. hot, cold, warm   _cold_   _warm_   _hot_

2. big, huge, small

3. dirty, filthy, dusty

4. upset, angry, livid

5. dry, wet, damp

6. frantic, calm, lively

7. frigid, cool, cold

8. stupendous, great, large

9. tragic, lucky, unfortunate

10. loud, silent, quiet

11. exorbitant, costly, moderate

12. precise, accurate, incorrect

13. unknown, familiar, intimate

14. shocking, frightful, hideous

15. popular, unliked, infamous

16. cowardly, bold, timid

17. exhausted, fatigued, tired

18. amusing, hilarious, funny

19. unhappy, inconsolable, distressed

20. perfect, adequate, deficient

21. generous, extravagant, frugal

22. outstanding, satisfactory, noteworthy

23. painstaking, careful, negligent

24. mortified, embarrassed, humiliated

25. urgent, unimportant, pressing

I.E.P. Goal: The client will arrange groups of descriptive words in relative order, with 90% or greater accuracy.

Copyright © 1988 LinguiSystems, Inc.

Task N: Comparing Historical Events — Temporal Relationships

Choose the correct answer for each question. The first one is done for you.

1. Which happened first, the stone age or the modern age?

   <u>stone age</u>   modern age

2. Which was invented first, the airplane or the train?

   airplane   train

3. Which happened first, landing a man on the moon or Columbus' voyage?

   landing a man on the moon   Columbus' voyage

4. Which happened more recently, the Civil War or the *Declaration of Independence*?

   Civil War   *Declaration of Independence*

5. Who lived in America first, the Pilgrims or the Native Americans?

   Pilgrims   Native Americans

6. Which was constructed first, the Empire State Building or the pyramids?

   Empire State Building   pyramids

7. Which happened first, the discovery of electricity or the invention of the television?

   discovery of electricity   invention of television

8. Which was put into use more recently, the tape recorder or the video cassette recorder?

   tape recorder   video cassette recorder

9. Who was born last, Abraham Lincoln or General Eisenhower?

   Abraham Lincoln   General Eisenhower

10. Which occurred earlier, World War II or the Vietnam conflict?

    World War II   Vietnam conflict

11. Who died more recently, Mark Twain or Thomas Jefferson?

    Mark Twain   Thomas Jefferson

12. Which happened more recently, the Wright brothers' flight or Custer's last stand?

    Wright brothers' flight   Custer's last stand

I.E.P. Goal: The client will answer questions comparing two historical events, with 90% or greater accuracy.

Task N: Comparing Historical Events — Temporal Relationships, *continued*

Choose the correct answer for each question.

13. Which was written first, the *United States Constitution* or the *Gettysburg Address*?

    United States Constitution   *Gettysburg Address*

14. Who lived earlier, Robert E. Lee or George Washington?

    Robert E. Lee   George Washington

15. Which was created first, the printing press or the microcomputer?

    printing press   microcomputer

16. Which mode of travel was used first, the steamboat or the sailboat?

    steamboat   sailboat

17. Which happened more recently, the coronation of Queen Elizabeth II or the inauguration of President Reagan?

    coronation of Queen Elizabeth II   inauguration of President Reagan

18. Which state joined the United States more recently, Alaska or Alabama?

    Alaska   Alabama

19. Which city is older, Rome or Washington, D.C.?

    Rome   Washington, D.C.

20. Which medical procedure was used first, heart transplants or limb amputations?

    heart transplants   limb amputations

21. Who was elected President more recently, John Kennedy or Harry Truman?

    John Kennedy   Harry Truman

22. Which happened first, the sinking of the *Titanic* or the explosion of the *Challenger*?

    sinking of the *Titanic*   explosion of the *Challenger*

23. Which happened last, the first Olympics or the World Series?

    first Olympics   World Series

24. Which vaccine was introduced first, smallpox or polio?

    smallpox   polio

I.E.P. Goal: The client will answer questions comparing two historical events, with 90% or greater accuracy.

Task O: Answering Relational Questions — Two Variables

Answer yes or no to these questions. The first one is done for you.

1. Can John be both taller and older than Dorothy?   <u>yes</u>   no

2. Can Andy be both older and younger than Troy?   yes   no

3. Can Harry be heavier than Ethan but not taller?   yes   no

4. Can water be both in a glass and under it?   yes   no

5. Can dust be both on a table and over it?   yes   no

6. Can Jim be both in front of Carl and beside him?   yes   no

7. Can Linda be smarter than Ellen but not older?   yes   no

8. Can a candle be both short and tall?   yes   no

9. If a ribbon is tied around a package, does it go under it?   yes   no

10. Can someone be both first and last in a line of people?   yes   no

11. Can the sun be over the clouds but not behind them?   yes   no

12. If a ship is sailing on the ocean, is the ship in the ocean?   yes   no

13. If a car drives over a bridge, is the car on the road?   yes   no

14. If today is warmer than yesterday, is it also cooler?   yes   no

15. If you walk beyond the school, do you pass it?   yes   no

16. If a book is on the table, is it next to the table?   yes   no

17. If a rug is beneath your feet, are you on the rug?   yes   no

18. If Kate is at the door, is she near it?   yes   no

19. Does your belt fit around both your waist and your wrist?   yes   no

20. Can Barbara be both smaller and older than David?   yes   no

21. If you drive across a bridge, do you drive below it?   yes   no

22. Can a Ping-Pong ball be bigger than a marble but not heavier?   yes   no

23. If you pour milk on cereal, is the milk in the cereal bowl?   yes   no

24. If you ride through a tunnel, do you ride around it?   yes   no

25. If a rope is inside the car, does it surround the car?   yes   no

I.E.P. Goal: When presented with relational questions containing two variables, the client will answer yes or no, with 90% or greater accuracy.

Basic Concepts: General Activities

1. Give the client pictures showing different seasonal events (e.g., swimming, snow skiing, planting a garden, various holidays) and instruct him to match the activities with the seasons. Show the client pictures of clothing worn during various seasons and ask him to match the clothing with the appropriate season.

2. Give the client blank weekly schedules and ask him to make out a personal schedule, using words or pictures to represent daily activities. Then, make up mythical schedules for important persons or fictional characters.

3. Using maps and actual timetables from airlines, trains, buses, or subways, have the client assume the role of travel agent and schedule trips to and from various points.

4. Write the names of simple tasks (e.g., tying one's shoes or saying the *Pledge of Allegiance*) on slips of paper. If working individually, ask the client to guess, in seconds, how long it will take him to perform the activity at a normal pace. Time him with a stopwatch and keep a record of how close he comes to guessing the actual time. If working in a group, keep team scores. The team with the total time closest to the actual time wins. Later, present the group with a list of the same tasks and ask them to order the tasks from the shortest to the longest times necessary for their completion.

5. For younger children, give an incorrect direction using a spatial preposition (e.g., "Put your sweater *under* your shoulders."). Let them try to carry out the direction, or explain why it cannot be done. Then, let the children give you silly directions.

6. Give the client an actual television schedule and a list of shows to watch that evening. Ask him to write or tell you what channel he will be watching for every half-hour slot from 7 to 11 P.M. Make the task more difficult by listing two shows which are aired simultaneously on different channels or which are not shown in the given time slot.

7. Use maps or a globe to work on directional spatial relationships. Ask questions such as, "In which direction should you travel to get from Florida to New York?" Use only north/south, east/west choices initially. Then, introduce concepts of northeast, southwest, etc.

8. For very young children, place a sticker, piece of yarn, etc. on a certain part of a child's body at the beginning of the day. For example, place a sticker *on* her back or *under* her cuff or tie a piece of yarn *in* her hair. Have the child look in a mirror and tell the location of the sticker. Then, throughout the day, ask, "Where is your sticker?" This task allows repeated practice of the spatial prepositions.

9. For very young children, place a different obstacle in front of the classroom door each morning. After they get through the obstacle, ask them what they did to enter the room. For example, have them crawl *under* a sliding board, *through* a hula hoop, *over* a jump rope, *around* a chair, *through* crepe paper streamers, etc.

10. Present the students with the list of ingredients for a recipe. Ask them to guess what the items will make when combined. Write down each person's guess. When the recipe is done, taste it and see who was correct!

11. Do simple science experiments which require events to be timed. Let the students keep time of the events using a stopwatch, egg timer or kitchen timer. Science experiments also may be used to discover basic attributes of items (e.g., Does it sink or float?; Will a magnet attract it or not?; Does it stretch without breaking?). These basic attributes can then be discussed and verbal comparisons can be made.

12. For young children, use different modes of response to make picture sequencing more appealing. Instead of simply arranging the pictures on a table in order, hang them on a clothesline in sequence, mail them in a mailbox in the appropriate order, or send them on a makeshift conveyor belt in the correct sequence. Use instant print film to take pictures of the child performing a sequential activity. Then, let the child arrange the photos and tell how she performed the activity. Use simple but fun activities that could be done at home (e.g., coloring eggs, making play dough, planting bulbs). Send the photos home with the child so the activity can be repeated.

13. Let older students or adults plan a party, deciding what quantity of each item is needed for the number of students. Give them basic information such as the number of cups per package or how many glasses of soda can be poured from a one liter bottle. After the party, let them see what items are left. Discuss why they might not have had enough of some things or had too much of others.

Paraphrasing

Paraphrasing involves rewording spoken or written language. In order to paraphrase, a speaker or writer must understand an original communication well enough to translate it into different words that mean the same thing.

Paraphrasing is an essential communication skill with everyday applications. Parents and teachers often use paraphrasing to explain an unfamiliar vocabulary word or expression to a child in a way the child can easily understand. Young children can often "say the same thing another way," as long as the message deals with their everyday experiences or common social expressions. Students often paraphrase information from reference materials in writing reports. Conversation partners often restate a message in a different way in order to either help a listener understand better, or to confirm the understanding of what another person has said.

In this section, various activities are designed to build skills in paraphrasing, including identifying synonyms and antonyms, determining the accuracy of paraphrased statements, and paraphrasing statements and paragraphs. The tasks progress in complexity. Skillful use of this section will allow the client to be flexible in understanding and using everyday language.

Paraphrasing
Task A: Identifying Synonyms

Find the two words in each group with similar meanings. The first one is done for you.

1.	healthy	<u>sick</u>	<u>ill</u>	ugly
2.	boat	automobile	car	plane
3.	cool	cloudy	toasty	chilly
4.	new	antique	old	salty
5.	garbage	bookshelf	trash	light bulb
6.	popular	rich	poor	wealthy
7.	fat	trim	overweight	tall
8.	tired	rested	sick	fatigued
9.	thin	happy	glad	sad
10.	big	rough	tiny	large
11.	ugly	harmless	beautiful	attractive
12.	afraid	favorite	frightened	last
13.	hungry	funny	boring	amusing
14.	intelligent	energetic	smart	expensive
15.	delightful	charming	disgusting	alarming
16.	soft	handy	convenient	clumsy
17.	moist	dry	damp	smelly
18.	easy	hard	funny	difficult
19.	gentle	mild	harsh	alert
20.	lift	lower	light	raise
21.	long	thick	dense	thin
22.	donate	remove	open	give
23.	stale	fresh	new	beautiful
24.	high	late	early	tardy
25.	firm	flexible	stiff	smooth

I.E.P. Goal: When presented with lists of four words, the client will identify the two synonyms, with 90% or greater accuracy.

Find the two words in each group with similar meanings.

26.	whole	broken	fragmented	heavy
27.	honest	truthful	unjust	fearless
28.	obedient	deviant	compliant	objectionable
29.	erroneous	accurate	lengthy	correct
30.	prejudiced	fair	objective	angry
31.	physician	artist	doctor	engineer
32.	mature	sinister	risky	ripe
33.	simple	difficult	complex	sturdy
34.	college	high school	university	kindergarten
35.	hardy	pale	flushed	ashen
36.	opponent	friend	enemy	employee
37.	slow	prompt	late	punctual
38.	interpret	inspect	explain	reject
39.	cowardice	patience	intelligence	endurance
40.	participate	anticipate	eject	expect
41.	work	reimburse	address	pay
42.	fictional	real	imaginary	flammable
43.	loss	profit	balance	gain
44.	isolated	friendly	alone	poor
45.	fraternal	maternal	natural	motherly
46.	perfect	stupid	infallible	keen
47.	outrageous	humble	modest	sickening
48.	convalesce	imitate	decline	recuperate
49.	trio	duet	triad	solo
50.	amazed	somber	elated	serious

I.E.P. Goal: When presented with lists of four words, the client will identify the two synonyms, with 90% or greater accuracy.

Task B: Identifying Antonyms

Find the two words in each group with opposite meanings. The first one is done for you.

1. <u>up</u>	in	<u>down</u>	behind
2. green	black	purple	white
3. noisy	sad	wet	quiet
4. sick	old	ill	new
5. right	top	middle	left
6. dry	cloudy	wet	windy
7. plain	light	heavy	easy
8. day	dusk	year	night
9. kind	cruel	happy	ill
10. swim	go	come	hop
11. empty	careful	depressed	full
12. married	short	sweet	tall
13. big	wide	little	bumpy
14. smart	rude	polite	drunk
15. child	brother	adult	family
16. father	friend	brother	enemy
17. dull	kind	sharp	silly
18. child	female	male	mate
19. forward	below	backward	around
20. part	classy	indistinct	whole
21. safe	dangerous	shiny	smelly
22. modern	quick	slow	round
23. repair	deliver	adjust	break
24. steady	single	jerky	disgraceful
25. strict	considerate	sturdy	thoughtless

I.E.P. Goal: When presented with lists of four words, the client will identify the two antonyms, with 90% or greater accuracy.

Task B: Identifying Antonyms, *continued*

Find the two words in each group with opposite meanings.

26. wrong	clever	destructive	correct
27. successful	same	different	artificial
28. positive	risky	suburban	negative
29. purchase	condone	admit	deny
30. strict	lenient	sour	clever
31. secondary	interior	primary	exterior
32. genuine	fancy	fake	lovely
33. responsible	sturdy	patient	fragile
34. absurd	firm	sensible	helpful
35. helpful	unusual	common	sensitive
36. defeat	victory	craze	vigilance
37. praise	practice	criticize	observe
38. proud	painful	ornate	pleasant
39. illegal	vertical	horizontal	limited
40. cheap	talented	serious	humorous
41. hidden	impressive	obvious	poor
42. engaged	elated	ugly	dismayed
43. conceal	construct	identify	censor
44. transfer	irrigate	object	agree
45. pale	coordinated	timid	clumsy
46. critical	greedy	generous	determined
47. capable	decisive	comfortable	incompetent
48. conservative	quick	fast	liberal
49. boring	interesting	moody	unsteady
50. clear	solid	ambiguous	clammy

I.E.P. Goal: When presented with lists of four words, the client will identify the two antonyms, with 90% or greater accuracy.

Task C: Discriminating Synonyms and Antonyms

Find the word that doesn't belong in each group. The first one is done for you.

1.	speedy	fast	<u>slow</u>
2.	curly	straight	wavy
3.	sour	tart	sweet
4.	hard	simple	easy
5.	uneven	bumpy	smooth
6.	small	huge	giant
7.	fancy	plain	bare
8.	fat	chubby	thin
9.	soft	spongy	hard
10.	loud	silent	quiet
11.	serious	silly	funny
12.	merry	jolly	sorry
13.	starving	hungry	full
14.	clear	muddy	cloudy
15.	crispy	doughy	crunchy
16.	boring	dull	exciting
17.	ancient	old	young
18.	cold	warm	icy
19.	sharp	pointed	curved
20.	friendly	stuck-up	outgoing
21.	clean	messy	neat
22.	dry	wet	damp
23.	cool	hot	burning
24.	small	tiny	large
25.	airy	stuffy	breezy

I.E.P Goal: When presented with lists of synonyms and antonyms, the client will choose the antonyms, with 90% or greater accuracy.

Task C: Discriminating Synonyms and Antonyms, *continued*

Find the word that doesn't belong in each group.

26. smooth	creased	wrinkled	folded
27. dirty	messy	rumpled	tidy
28. blank	empty	full	bare
29. gentle	rough	tough	hard
30. weak	husky	muscular	strong
31. worried	confident	fearful	concerned
32. sad	depressed	unhappy	elated
33. courteous	rude	impolite	crude
34. lively	energetic	dull	enthusiastic
35. cheap	expensive	costly	high-priced
36. sturdy	brittle	breakable	fragile
37. confined	restrained	free	imprisoned
38. tall	lanky	short	gangling
39. flexible	stubborn	firm	tough
40. offensive	appealing	foul	disgusting
41. immature	childish	infantile	mature
42. specific	precise	exact	inaccurate
43. gentle	rough	tender	mild
44. cheerful	lively	angry	jovial
45. tasty	flavorful	bland	delicious
46. healthy	ill	well	fit
47. miniature	large	bulky	huge
48. tired	weary	energetic	fatigued
49. attractive	plain	handsome	beautiful
50. thin	husky	slender	willowy

I.E.P Goal: When presented with lists of synonyms and antonyms, the client will choose the antonyms, with 90% or greater accuracy.

Task D: Identifying Similar Words

Find the word on the right that is most similar to the word on the left. The first one is done for you.

1. police officer	<u>sheriff</u>	fire fighter	mail carrier
2. doughnut	cupcake	bagel	pie
3. handkerchief	necktie	sash	tissue
4. blanket	pillow	quilt	bathrobe
5. coat	hat	shirt	jacket
6. scissors	clippers	knife	razor blade
7. doormat	rug	doorbell	doorknob
8. pencil	ruler	crayon	paintbrush
9. cafeteria	gymnasium	kitchen	restaurant
10. pliers	hammer	wrench	screwdriver
11. hose	pipe	clamp	sponge
12. theater	church	auditorium	classroom
13. nest	mailbox	pocket	cradle
14. helmet	hard hat	earmuffs	sombrero
15. mug	cup	pan	bowl
16. mule	goat	tiger	horse
17. infant	adult	teenager	baby
18. eraser	ink	spot remover	chewing gum
19. diary	magazine	calendar	dictionary
20. tongs	tweezers	ice pick	ladle

I.E.P. Goal: When presented with an item and a list of related words, the client will choose the most similar word, with 90% or greater accuracy.

Find the word on the right that is most similar to the word on the left.

21. clock	hourglass	watch	sundial
22. boat	train	plane	surfboard
23. curtains	sheets	blinds	screen
24. work	job	interview	money
25. lock	key	latch	door
26. picture	photograph	camera	film
27. spoon	wheel	knife	ladle
28. shelf	box	cabinet	ledge
29. field	playground	pasture	garden
30. tape	Band-Aid	glue	staple
31. ditch	dirt	hole	trench
32. cash register	microwave	adding machine	typewriter
33. cucumber	pickle	squash	lettuce
34. journal	leaflet	memo	magazine
35. song	shout	tune	speech
36. dog	lion	tiger	coyote
37. taxi	tricycle	bus	sailboat
38. medicine	soap	prescription	ambulance
39. path	trail	atmosphere	hallway
40. architect	lawyer	banker	designer

I.E.P. Goal: When presented with an item and a list of related words, the client will choose the most similar word, with 90% or greater accuracy.

Task E: Identifying Associated Words

Underline all the words in each group that go together. Then, write how they go together in the blanks. The first one is done for you.

1. <u>bat</u>, <u>mitt</u>, goggles   _____baseball things_____

2. crown, glove, hat   _____

3. oil, satin, linen   _____

4. corn, apple, oats   _____

5. sapphire, ruby, copper   _____

6. bracelet, necklace, watch   _____

7. puck, racquet, airplane, chocolate   _____

8. sheets, ax, drill, pliers   _____

9. letter, banjo, anchor, trumpet   _____

10. hornet, nail, game, bee   _____

11. broccoli, shamrocks, peas, chain   _____

12. reading, desk, physics, mathematics   _____

13. science, Thanksgiving, Easter, New Year's   _____

14. cheese, oval, cake, triangle   _____

15. tracks, caboose, cement, locomotive   _____

16. algebra, stapler, paper clip, lettuce   _____

17. Earth, Baptist, Jupiter, Washington   _____

18. Monopoly, kickball, songs, checkers   _____

19. "hop," "ding," "boom," "pop"   _____

20. macadamia, window, hickory, candle   _____

21. fork, knife, box, light   _____

22. bucket, pool, canteen, flour   _____

23. chef, friend, artist, secretary   _____

24. chair, run, crawl, slide   _____

25. brick, rubber band, muscles, bubble gum   _____

I.E.P. Goal: The client will identify the words in a list that are associated and tell how, with 90% or greater accuracy.

Task E: Identifying Associated Words, *continued*

Find all the words in each group that go together. Then, tell how the words are related.

26. Saturn, Idaho, Vermont, Illinois _____

27. Colorado, Mexico, Peru, Paris _____

28. hepatitis, horseshoes, chicken pox, tacos _____

29. brass, bronze, silver, basket _____

30. Andy, Ted, Cindy, Carl _____

31. sonnet, waltz, tango, perfume _____

32. fish, sparrow, crab, octopus _____

33. parrot, spider, gardenia, dove _____

34. pen, paint, pencil, key _____

35. ice, fire, sun, leaves _____

36. cookies, cider, gum, soda _____

37. snake, calf, chicken, sheep _____

38. magazine, table, couch, chair _____

39. snorkel, watch, airplane, bicycle _____

40. book, magazine, sign, cupcake _____

41. poppy, daffodil, celery, tulip _____

42. robin, raccoon, airplane, butterfly _____

43. ball, marble, box, pearl _____

44. heart, foot, brain, liver _____

45. grapefruit, milk, kiwi, lime _____

46. glue, mayonnaise, turpentine, jelly _____

47. ax, noun, verb, adjective _____

48. carnival, burglary, canopy, larceny _____

49. Democratic, Libra, Independent, Republican _____

50. sympathy, fear, remorse, conversation _____

I.E.P. Goal: The client will identify the words in a list that are related or associated and tell how, with 90% or greater accuracy.

Task F: Yes/No Response for Paraphrased Words in Descriptive Statements

Answer yes or no to each question. The first one is done for you.

1. If someone is starving, is he hungry? <u>yes</u> no

2. If something is simple, is it hard? yes no

3. If someone is fast, is she quick? yes no

4. If someone is fearful, is she confident? yes no

5. If something is an antique, is it old? yes no

6. If something is straight, does it have curves? yes no

7. If someone is tardy, is he early? yes no

8. If a painting is strange, is it unusual? yes no

9. If someone is depressed, is he happy? yes no

10. If a door is ajar, is it open? yes no

11. If someone is obese, is she thin? yes no

12. If someone is generous, is he giving? yes no

13. If water is lukewarm, is it cold? yes no

14. If a table is sturdy, is it wobbly? yes no

15. If someone is feverish, is he ill? yes no

16. If someone is verbose, is he talkative? yes no

17. If someone is ornery, is he agreeable? yes no

18. If someone is reimbursed, is he paid? yes no

19. If something is interesting, is it boring? yes no

20. If something is significant, is it noteworthy? yes no

21. If something is intercepted, does it reach its original destination? yes no

22. If something is cancelled, is it terminated? yes no

23. If something is done manually, is it done by machine? yes no

24. If someone is incompetent, is she capable? yes no

25. If someone is presumptuous, is she assuming? yes no

I.E.P. Goal: When presented with questions concerning descriptions of persons or things, the client will respond yes or no, with 90% or greater accuracy.

Task G: Yes/No Response for Paraphrased Common Expressions

Answer yes or no to each question. The first one is done for you.

1. If someone has a *heart of gold*, is she kind?   <u>yes</u>   no

2. If someone is *fit as a fiddle*, is he ill?   yes   no

3. If someone is *longwinded*, is she talkative?   yes   no

4. If something is *clean as a whistle*, is it dirty?   yes   no

5. If someone is *bored to tears*, is he excited?   yes   no

6. If someone is a *nitpicker*, is he concerned with details?   yes   no

7. If someone is *raring to go*, is he enthusiastic?   yes   no

8. If someone is *fit to be tied*, is he relaxed?   yes   no

9. If someone is *green with envy*, is he jealous?   yes   no

10. If someone is *happy go lucky*, is she depressed?   yes   no

11. If someone is *sharp as a tack*, is he smart?   yes   no

12. If something is *tried and true*, is it novel?   yes   no

13. If someone has a *green thumb*, is she talented?   yes   no

14. If an office is *run by the book*, do the employees have much freedom?   yes   no

15. If something is done *as quick as a flash*, is it done instantly?   yes   no

16. If someone is *over a barrel*, is he in a predicament?   yes   no

17. If someone *has it made in the shade*, is he having problems?   yes   no

18. If someone is *as old as the hills*, is she immature?   yes   no

19. If someone *gets under your skin*, is he irritating?   yes   no

20. If someone is *painfully shy*, is she extroverted?   yes   no

21. If someone is *set in his ways*, is he inflexible?   yes   no

22. If someone is a *snake in the grass*, is he trustworthy?   yes   no

23. If someone is a *jack of all trades*, is he clever?   yes   no

24. If someone *bugs you* often, does he irritate you?   yes   no

25. If someone is *as happy as a lark*, is she in a good mood?   yes   no

I.E.P. Goal: The client will agree or disagree with the correctness of paraphrasings of common sayings, with 90% or greater accuracy.

Answer yes or no to each question.

26.	If someone is *as white as a ghost*, is he flushed?	yes	no
27.	If something is *as slick as grease*, is it smooth?	yes	no
28.	If something is *as hot as blazes*, is it cold?	yes	no
29.	If someone is *as smooth as silk*, is he polite?	yes	no
30.	If someone is *as cool as ice*, is she easily upset?	yes	no
31.	If something is *razor sharp*, is it dull?	yes	no
32.	If someone is *as quiet as a mouse*, is she shy?	yes	no
33.	If someone is *broken hearted*, is he happy?	yes	no
34.	If someone is a *sourpuss*, is he grumpy?	yes	no
35.	If something is *as light as a feather*, is it heavy?	yes	no
36.	If something is *cut and dried*, is it routine?	yes	no
37.	If someone is *as thin as a rail*, is she overweight?	yes	no
38.	If an idea is *half-baked*, is it a good one?	yes	no
39.	If something is *as clear as mud*, is it confusing?	yes	no
40.	If someone is *as sick as a dog*, is he healthy?	yes	no
41.	If someone's *bark is worse than his bite*, is he nicer than he appears?	yes	no
42.	If someone is *as busy as a beaver*, is he lazy?	yes	no
43.	If a house is *as neat as a pin*, is it dusty?	yes	no
44.	If someone is *as happy as a clam*, is he having fun?	yes	no
45.	If something *stands the test of time*, is it obsolete?	yes	no
46.	If a horse *runs like the wind*, is it swift?	yes	no
47.	If someone is *sick to death* of something, is he dissatisfied?	yes	no
48.	If something is *as easy as pie*, is it difficult?	yes	no
49.	If someone has to *pay the piper*, is he responsible?	yes	no
50.	If someone is *as solid as a rock*, is he dependable?	yes	no

I.E.P. Goal: The client will agree or disagree with the correctness of paraphrasings of common sayings, with 90% or greater accuracy.

Task H: Paraphrasing Words in Sentences

Rephrase each sentence, replacing the underlined word with a word or phrase that means the same thing. The first one is done for you.

1. Jerome is <u>sick</u>.

    Jerome is ill.

2. Randa is <u>pretty</u>.

    _____

3. Wendy was <u>cold</u> sitting outside.

    _____

4. Chad wanted to <u>speak</u> to the police officer.

    _____

5. Tom was <u>glad</u> to see his mom.

    _____

6. Jan was too <u>angry</u> to listen.

    _____

7. Len was <u>scared</u> of ghosts.

    _____

8. Ben <u>ripped</u> the paper.

    _____

9. An elephant is <u>big</u>.

    _____

10. Fred got the job done <u>quickly</u>.

    _____

11. The wading pool is <u>shallow</u>.

    _____

12. This steak is <u>tough</u>.

    _____

I.E.P. Goal: The client will replace a specific word in a sentence while maintaining the same sentence meaning, with 90% or greater accuracy.

Rephrase each sentence, replacing the underlined word or phrase that means the same thing.

13. The bread was <u>fresh</u>.

_____

14. Lou's statement was <u>false</u>.

_____

15. Mary is very <u>generous</u>.

_____

16. The ceremony is about to <u>commence</u>.

_____

17. The food in that restaurant is <u>expensive</u>.

_____

18. The baby's bib was <u>damp</u>.

_____

19. The chest of drawers is an <u>antique</u>.

_____

20. The trail was very <u>dangerous</u>.

_____

21. The restroom was <u>sanitary</u>.

_____

22. The presentation was <u>complete</u>.

_____

23. The slaves wanted <u>liberty</u>.

_____

24. This novel is <u>fiction</u>.

_____

I.E.P. Goal: The client will replace a specific word in a sentence while maintaining the same sentence meaning, with 90% or greater accuracy.

Task H: Paraphrasing Words in Sentences, *continued*

Rephrase each sentence, replacing the underlined word or phrase that means the same thing.

25. That picture is <u>ugly</u>.

_____

26. The store manager is <u>busy</u>.

_____

27. Maddie is <u>rich</u>.

_____

28. Carl went <u>away</u>.

_____

29. Frank said the job was <u>temporary</u>.

_____

30. The pond water was <u>clear</u>.

_____

31. The new bus schedules are <u>different</u>.

_____

32. Katie is <u>greedy</u>.

_____

33. The secretary's typing was <u>perfect</u>.

_____

34. Brian's comment was very <u>degrading</u>.

_____

35. This material is <u>flammable</u>.

_____

36. The disease is very <u>contagious</u>.

_____

I.E.P. Goal: The client will replace a specific word in a sentence while maintaining the same sentence meaning, with 90% or greater accuracy.

Task I: Paraphrasing Common Sayings

Rephrase each sentence using different words that mean the same thing as the underlined words. The first one is done for you.

1. The lake looks <u>as smooth as glass</u>.

   _____

2. I think Bob got up on the <u>wrong side of the bed this morning</u>.

   _____

3. <u>Feast your eyes</u> on that sunset.

   _____

4. I need another job <u>like I need a hole in the head</u>.

   _____

5. When I lost the election, Dad told me to <u>keep a stiff upper lip</u>.

   _____

6. I have <u>butterflies in my stomach</u>.

   _____

7. Sandra was <u>as pleased as punch</u>.

   _____

8. Norman is <u>as quiet as a church mouse</u>.

   _____

9. Ted treats me <u>as if I were born yesterday</u>.

   _____

10. My teacher really makes us <u>tow the line</u>.

    _____

11. This math is <u>as easy as pie</u>.

    _____

12. Our new TV <u>cost us an arm and a leg</u>.

    _____

I.E.P. Goal: The client will paraphrase common sayings in sentence contexts, with 90% or greater accuracy.

Task I: Paraphrasing Common Sayings, *continued*

Rephrase each sentence using different words that mean the same thing as the underlined words.

13. If Ed doesn't take that job, he'll be <u>cutting his own throat</u>.

_____

14. When my brakes failed, I thought <u>my number was up</u> for sure.

_____

15. My grandma always says <u>to live and let live</u>.

_____

16. Now that her children are gone, she's <u>as free as a bird</u>.

_____

17. Jean has her <u>fingers in too many pies</u>.

_____

18. I love Karen as if she were <u>my own flesh and blood</u>.

_____

19. George acts as if he has <u>one foot in the grave</u>.

_____

20. That's the <u>long and the short of</u> what happened at the fair.

_____

21. Mr. Henderson is a <u>wolf in sheep's clothing</u>.

_____

22. My uncle looked <u>like a fish out of water</u> at the wedding reception.

_____

23. Lisa looks like <u>the cat who swallowed the canary</u>.

_____

24. We got this china <u>for a song</u> at a yard sale.

_____

I.E.P. Goal: The client will paraphrase common sayings in sentence contexts, with 90% or greater accuracy.

Task I: Paraphrasing Common Sayings, *continued*

Rephrase each sentence using different words that mean the same thing as the underlined words.

25. Suzanne certainly is <u>light on her feet</u>.

   _____

26. Taking care of the baby is <u>easier said than done</u>.

   _____

27. <u>For the life of me</u>, I don't know where I put my address book.

   _____

28. Their marriage doesn't seem to have been <u>made in heaven</u>.

   _____

29. Lee is a <u>Johnny-on-the-spot</u>.

   _____

30. The main character in this novel is <u>as mad as a hatter</u>.

   _____

31. Our neighbors moved out of their house, <u>lock, stock and barrel</u>.

   _____

32. If you tell him what I said, it will just <u>add fuel to the fire</u>.

   _____

33. I'll let you drive my new car <u>when donkeys fly</u>!

   _____

34. I heard the Stevens' new business is <u>on the ropes</u>.

   _____

35. The children gathered around the storyteller <u>like moths to a flame</u>.

   _____

36. I <u>went through fire and water</u> to get tickets for the playoff game.

I.E.P. Goal: The client will paraphrase common sayings in sentence contexts, with 90% or greater accuracy.

Task J: Paraphrasing Statements

Rephrase each sentence using different words to mean the same thing. The first one is done for you.

1. I could sit through that movie five more times.

   I really liked the movie.

2. It will be a cold day in summer before I go to that restaurant again.

   _____

3. Children drive me up the wall.

   _____

4. I am in awe of Ms. Correlli.

   _____

5. I don't care if I ever see the Richardsons again!

   _____

6. I thought the history exam was a piece of cake.

   _____

7. I'm annoyed that my sister asked me to do her laundry.

   _____

8. I think my pediatrician is tops!

   _____

9. Deciding what to wear to the party is the least of my worries.

   _____

10. I would give my eye teeth to go to England.

    _____

11. If I don't get some help with this job, I'll scream!

    _____

12. Mr. Nelson gave me the runaround.

    _____

I.E.P. Goal: The client will paraphrase statements, with 90% or greater accuracy.

Task J: Paraphrasing Statements, *continued*

Rephrase each sentence using different words to mean the same thing.

13. Joel always acts as if he has a chip on his shoulder.

_____

14. You're not really going to wear that dress to the wedding, are you?

_____

15. I feel like I'm running on empty.

_____

16. You can buy that stereo for a song.

_____

17. Lynn is nice, but she's not playing with a full deck.

_____

18. All I can say is, my hands are tied.

_____

19. Jose is certainly not another Picasso.

_____

20. Don't you think that's putting the cart before the horse?

_____

21. I wish I had a dime for every book I've loaned to a friend and lost.

_____

22. Unless I get a raise, we'll have to tighten our belts.

_____

23. Public speaking is not Allen's strong suit.

_____

24. Let's prioritize our activities for today.

_____

I.E.P. Goal: The client will paraphrase statements, with 90% or greater accuracy.

Task K: Using Logic or Exclusion to Make Deductions

Read each sentence. Then, tell the information you know that wasn't stated in the sentence. The first one is done for you.

1. There is poison ivy growing around the trees at the back of our yard.

   We should stay away from the back of our yard.

2. Karen didn't get sick until Saturday.

   _____

3. I invited only three girls and David to the party.

   _____

4. If it rains on Thursday, we'll hold the event indoors.

   _____

5. Don't wear hard-soled shoes on the boat.

   _____

6. Everyone has checked in except Ben.

   _____

7. We went to the shore every summer when I was a child.

   _____

8. Don't put any mustard on my hot dog.

   _____

9. The Lehman's lights are on and their car is in the driveway.

   _____

10. If the film is exposed to light, it will be ruined.

    _____

11. I waited at the cafe for fifteen minutes, but you didn't show up.

    _____

12. Joy is the valedictorian of her senior class.

    _____

I.E.P. Goal: The client will provide additional information implied, but not stated, in the original statements, with 90% or greater accuracy.

Task K: Using Logic or Exclusion to Make Deductions, *continued*

Read each sentence. Then, tell the information you know that wasn't stated in the sentence.

13. The problem was heavy on everyone's mind.

_____

14. Lily will do anything to appease her parents.

_____

15. Maude doesn't participate in interscholastic contests.

_____

16. Mr. LePeter and his business partners are guilty of fraud.

_____

17. The painter used diluted paint for his portrait.

_____

18. English was Mr. Damien's second language.

_____

19. The cabin was secluded by the trees and rocks.

_____

20. The professor was not very articulate in his remarks.

_____

21. The tree clipping crew was very industrious.

_____

22. Dominic and Rosa had a harmonious relationship.

_____

23. Dr. Kurt has some very unorthodox views about practicing medicine.

_____

24. The corporation takeover was a calculated maneuver.

_____

I.E.P. Goal: The client will provide additional information implied, but not stated, in the original statements, with 90% or greater accuracy.

Task L: Paraphrasing Paragraphs

Retell the following paragraphs, including the most important information.

Note: For a written task, have the client rewrite each paragraph, replacing the underlined parts with words or phrases that mean the same thing. The first paragraph is done as an example.

1. Sharon and Lynn <u>decided to form</u> a secret club. First, they <u>picked</u> two friends to <u>join</u> them. These friends <u>thought the club was a great idea</u> and they helped <u>make up</u> a secret code. The club met <u>once a week</u> in Lynn's room. Sometimes they <u>talked about</u> their <u>favorite</u> books and movies. <u>Other times, they worked on special projects</u> such as <u>making gifts</u> to give their families for holidays.

   Sharon and Lynn wanted to start a secret club. First, they chose two friends to be in the club with them. These friends liked the idea of the club and they helped develop a secret code. The club met weekly in Lynn's room. Sometimes they discussed their most enjoyable books and movies. At other meetings, they worked on special tasks such as designing presents to give their families for holidays.

2. One of the <u>greatest joys of</u> life is <u>being a parent</u>. Although children <u>try your patience and keeping up with them is an exhausting job</u>, the <u>rewards</u> for your time are many. Children <u>appreciate the simple pleasures of life</u> and help us see things <u>just as they are</u>, not the way we wish they would be. And, <u>there is never a dull moment around a child</u>. They keep you <u>young at heart</u> even if the rest of you is <u>worn out!</u>

3. <u>Who could work through the hot summer months without</u> air conditioning? It is <u>difficult</u> to believe that employees could <u>be productive</u> working in <u>steaming</u> offices, before <u>the advent of air conditioning.</u> <u>It has been shown</u> that employees working in a pleasant environment are comfortable and can <u>generate more work</u> than those <u>not so fortunate.</u>

4. Although one might think so, writing a good book is not an <u>easy task</u>. It takes a lot of <u>dedication</u>, time and talent. There are rewrites, editing and <u>complete changes</u> in the <u>material</u>. <u>Timelines</u> must be followed and <u>strict attention to details is necessary.</u> The <u>finished product</u> is the <u>heart</u> and <u>soul</u> of the author...and then some!

I.E.P. Goal: The client will paraphrase complex paragraphs, with 90% or greater accuracy.

Task L: Paraphrasing Paragraphs, *continued*

Retell the following paragraphs, including the most important information.

Note: For a written task, have the client rewrite each paragraph, replacing the underlined parts with words or phrases that mean the same thing. The first paragraph on page 65 is done as an example.

5. Last year on spring break, several of my friends accompanied me to Vail, Colorado, to do a little skiing. Once there, we had a blizzard that left two feet of snow on the ground and left us stranded in our cabins for three days. We didn't mind, though, as it was fun curling up with a good book next to the roaring fire. Once we flew back to the coast when our break was over, we missed the solitude of the snow-covered mountains.

6. Daycare centers are popping up on every corner these days. More mothers are returning to the work force and need child care for their children. Daycare centers, though expensive, usually provide certified teachers, nutritious meals and snacks, as well as transportation after school for children. The centers are open extended hours to cater to the working family and are centrally located to allow visits by the parents during the workday.

7. If one plans ahead in the fall, spring can bring a bounty of beautiful flowers. Many spring flowering bulbs are available, including tulips, jonquils, daffodils and hyacinths. Although a bit of elbow grease is necessary to plant the bulbs deep enough to protect them from squirrels, the rewards are great. Seeing the first shoots peek through a late snow is a welcome sign of the warm weather which is sure to follow.

8. Where would the world be without the invention of the sewing machine? Not only can garments be made quicker, but the seams are sturdier. While everyone appreciates the beautiful handiwork of our grandmothers, the new fabrics and the need for practical, economical garments that can be obtained easily dictate the use of machinery.

9. When learning to drive a car, the best advice is to get a complete stranger to teach you. Relatives and friends are always willing to help out, but to let them is almost always a mistake. It is difficult for them to think of you as being either old enough or responsible enough to drive this vehicle called a car. A stranger will leave once the lesson is over, but your family or friends will be around to harass you about your mistakes for days on end. For those who can't afford private lessons and must rely on their families to teach them, it is a true miracle that they ever learn how to drive.

10. A favorite sport for many men and women is the game of golf. Not only is it relaxing for the keyed-up executive; it also allows for socializing with colleagues and business acquaintances in a low-stress environment. Aggressions can be taken out on the golf ball, rather than on one's friends. And, many a business deal has been struck during a game on the links. An executive looking for a sport in which to invest his limited time might consider golf for its many advantages.

I.E.P. Goal: The client will paraphrase complex paragraphs, with 90% or greater accuracy.

Task L: **Paraphrasing Paragraphs**, *continued*

Retell the following paragraphs, including the most important information.

Note: For a written task, have the client rewrite each paragraph, replacing the underlined parts with words or phrases that mean the same thing. The first paragraph on page 65 is done as an example.

11. <u>Good nutrition</u> has never been easier! No longer are our fruit and vegetable choices <u>confined</u> to canned or frozen <u>items</u>. Nowadays, grocery stores <u>compete</u> to see <u>who can stock</u> the freshest fruits and vegetables. Not only are the <u>traditional fruits and vegetables available</u>, but <u>exotic</u> varieties such as white asparagus, yellow peppers and tearless onions <u>can be found in</u> many stores. New <u>cooking methods</u> such as steaming or microwaving <u>help</u> to <u>ensure</u> that more nutrients remain in the produce during cooking. <u>With very little effort</u>, we can eat healthier and feel better.

12. Blue jeans <u>have come of age</u>! Fifty years ago, jeans were thought <u>to be at home</u> only <u>on the range</u> or <u>on the tractor</u>. Now, they are <u>seen everywhere</u>, on people of all ages and sizes. Grandmothers in designer jeans can be seen with their grandchildren, who <u>are likely to be wearing</u> baby-sized blue jean overalls. <u>Children of all ages each own</u> several pairs of jeans and, in many schools, blue jeans <u>serve as uniforms</u>. Clearly an item as durable and comfortable as blue jeans <u>is here to stay</u>!

13. When <u>having your car serviced</u>, you must first call the <u>repair shop</u> and make an appointment. Once you <u>have arrived there at your scheduled time</u>, you must fill out a service form <u>instructing</u> the service department <u>as to what your vehicle needs</u>. <u>For any major items to be done</u>, you should ask the service manager to <u>determine an estimate</u> of the cost before you <u>give your consent</u>. When your car is <u>finished</u>, the service department will give you a call so you can <u>pick it up</u>.

14. As winter <u>approaches</u>, our thoughts turn away from the <u>active pleasures</u> of summer toward quieter, indoor activities. Frisbees are put away in favor of jigsaw puzzles. The bathing suits and shorts in our <u>bureaus</u> are <u>packed away</u> to make room for sweaters and sweatshirts. Although <u>many winter sports are available</u> to keep us active, winter also is a good time to catch up on activities such as reading, knitting, writing letters and relaxing <u>in front of a cheery fire</u>.

15. Chocolate lovers of the world <u>have united</u>! No longer are our ice cream choices <u>limited</u> to chocolate and fudge ripple. <u>We now have</u> chocolate candy almond, chocolate rocky road, peanut butter and chocolate, and fudge brownie supreme <u>to choose from</u>. And, if we can't find an ice cream flavor to <u>please us</u>, we can <u>satisfy our sweet tooths</u> with cookies, fudge, brownies, or truffles. <u>Chocolate-covered ants, anyone</u>?

16. In the <u>past decade</u>, our society has <u>made much progress in accepting persons with special needs</u>. Students with handicaps <u>are now able</u> to take part in public school programs and have <u>contributed</u> much to their classmates and teachers. In the work place, adults with <u>disabilities</u> are found <u>filling many</u> different roles, such as teacher, bank president, cashier and attorney. What we all have learned from their <u>experiences</u> is that for handicapped persons, <u>just as for the rest of us</u>, what we can do is more important than what we cannot do!

I.E.P. Goal: The client will paraphrase complex paragraphs, with 90% or greater accuracy.

Retell the following paragraphs, including the most important information.

Note: For a written task, have the client rewrite each paragraph, replacing the underlined parts with words or phrases that mean the same thing. The first paragraph on page 65 is done as an example.

17. Building a bookshelf is a good project for a beginning carpenter. First, you must measure the space to decide what length the shelf will be. Next, a trip to the hardware store is in order to buy the wood, brackets and screws needed to build the shelf. Make sure the shelf is level before securing it to the wall — you don't want the books to slide off! A final coat of wood stain or paint to match the room will add the finishing touch to your project.

18. There are many different kinds of fabric available. Each type is best suited for a certain purpose. Silks and satins make dazzling evening gowns, while muslin and broadcloth make functional curtains or totebags. Stretch fabric helps athletes move easily and down-filled nylon jackets keep us warm in the coldest weather. Every color of the rainbow can be seen in samples of fabric. This large variety of colors is quite a contrast to the limited colors available to our ancestors, when natural vegetable dyes were the only source of fabric color available.

19. The grocery store in our neighborhood recently has been modernized. It now has a deli where shoppers can buy all kinds of meat and cheese and salads. The bakery department has fresh bread, rolls, doughnuts and bagels, and birthday cakes can be made-to-order. On one aisle, there is a selection of several types of coffee beans. Shoppers can choose the type they prefer and grind them fresh in the machine. In the back corner, there is a florist shop where arrangements and cut flowers may be purchased. All that is missing is someone to do your shopping for you!

20. At Grandma's house, there is a catch-all drawer which all the grandchildren love to look through when they go to visit. Almost anything from aspirin to zippers may be found in the drawer. The best things in the drawer are those which bring forth a story from Grandma, such as the buttons from Grandpa's army uniform or the photograph of the first group of pupils she taught in elementary school. One day I asked her why she kept an old plastic doll with one leg missing. She said it had been my favorite toy when I was two. Although the contents of the drawer may look like junk to most people, they are clearly Grandma's treasures!

21. Is there anyone alive who doesn't enjoy a circus? Who can resist the mix or surprise, beauty and danger a circus brings? Everyone has his own favorite part of a circus. For some it is the graceful acrobats, tightrope walkers and trapeze artists. Others prefer the thrill of watching the big animals as their trainers put them through their paces. Children love the colorful clowns as they race around the ring, chasing one another and playing tricks on the audience. The cotton candy and peanuts are added treats to an already jam-packed evening. No wonder so many people dream about running off to join the circus!

I.E.P. Goal: The client will paraphrase complex paragraphs, with 90% or greater accuracy.

Paraphrasing: General Activities

1. Have students pretend they are taking a visitor from a foreign country on a tour of their city or neighborhood. They must assume that the visitor has only a limited knowledge of English and translates everything very literally. Have the students make a booklet for the visitor which paraphrases common signs or sayings the visitor might encounter, such as: *Yield* (to slow down and give the right of way to another car); *no jaywalking* (don't cross the street in the middle of the block); *drive-thru window* (you may drive your car up to the restaurant window to order a hamburger); and *cafeteria* (a restaurant where you serve yourself food from a long counter). The students may want to spend a week or two noting and jotting down phrases they see in their environment before making their booklets.

2. Give students a paraphrased list of current songs. Have them rephrase each title to come up with the name of a popular song. For example, "The Day Before Today" becomes "Yesterday"; "The Flag Covered with Stars" becomes "The Star Spangled Banner"; and "Resting on the Pier in the Inlet" becomes "Sittin' on the Dock of the Bay." This can be an ongoing activity in which students see who can bring in titles which will stump the others. This same activity can be done with movie titles by presenting a box office hits list to be paraphrased. For example, "Sixty Thousand Nautical Miles below the Ocean" would become "Twenty Thousand Leagues under the Sea," "Mandibles" would become "Jaws," and "Deadly Charm" would become "Fatal Attraction." A "bestseller" list could be used for book titles.

3. Have students listen to television and radio commercials, taking notes about advertising slogans and names of products. Then, ask the students to paraphrase the names and slogans. For example, "I Can't Believe It's Not Butter" would become "It Doesn't Taste Like Margarine to Me," "Ouchless Band-Aids" becomes "Band-Aids That Don't Hurt When You Rip Them Off," and "Bet You Can't Pinch an Inch" becomes "This Cereal Is Not Fattening." A variation on this activity is to give students product descriptions or actual products and have them paraphrase the products' characteristics to come up with names for the products or advertising slogans.

4. Choose two or three topics for the day. Ask one client to whisper his opinion about that particular topic to the client sitting next to him. That client then turns to his neighbor and communicates what was said to him in his own words to his neighbor. Continue with the entire group until the final individual reports what client number one thought of the topic presented. A review of paraphrasings may be appropriate to hear the various ways the same idea can be communicated, as well as to discuss subtle changes in the meaning of the original message.

5. Present a topic to the group and ask one client to state his opinion of that topic. Have another client paraphrase what the first client said, without using any of the language used previously. Continue this process until no other paraphrasings are possible or until everyone has had a turn.

6. Using the items from Tasks I and J, provide the students with the paraphrased answer, such as, "My teacher really makes us work hard." Then, ask the students if they can generate a common saying or statement that says the same thing. The answer could be, "My math teacher really makes me tow the line," or "My math teacher really makes me put my nose to the grindstone."

7. Print common sayings or statements on cards. Have the group divide into three teams. The first team picks a card and discusses how to pantomime the statement to the other teams. One person on the first team then acts out the statement while the other two teams guess the statement. The first team to guess wins one point. After a designated period of time (thirty to sixty minutes), the team with the most points wins.

8. Use one-act plays. Have students read one-act plays silently, paying specific attention to the perspective of one character. Then, read a brief synopsis of the play out loud to the group. Call on individuals to interpret their character's opinion on the series of events to stimulate pragmatic skills, syntax and semantics.

9. Have your students pretend they will be explaining various topics to a four year old child. As a four year old does not have the experience level of an older child or an adult, this activity requires students to simplify concepts by paraphrasing. Sample topics could include: death of a pet, pregnancy, divorce, first day at school, thunderstorms, graduation, vacation, overnight business trips, etc. Respond to the students' comments, or invite a four year old to the session and allow her to interact directly with the students. Such discussions involve a tremendous amount of redirection, rephrasing and modification.

10. Give the students a key word and ask them to generate as many words as they can that have a similiar meaning. For each word, give sixty seconds to generate a list. Similarly, provide those same key words and ask students to generate as many words as they can that have opposite meanings. This activity may be put in a game format with points given for each word listed. The student with the most points wins. A team approach can also be implemented based on the same principle.

Critical Thinking

Critical thinking is a basic skill for daily living. Each day, we are faced with many problems of varying types and complexity. Our ability to solve these problems by matching them with appropriate solutions enables us to have control over our environment and, as a result, function as independent, competent individuals.

This unit provides practice with the full range of types and complexity of everyday situations requiring critical thinking. The tasks range from simply naming the items needed to do a common activity to identifying the multiple problems and solutions inherent in complex situations. The ultimate goal of these tasks is for the client to generalize effective critical thinking to his everyday environment.

Task A: Naming Items Needed to Perform Activities

List up to three things you need to do each activity below. The first one is done for you.

1.	scramble an egg	*egg*	*frying pan*	*spatula*
2.	send a letter			
3.	fly a kite			
4.	bake a cake			
5.	take a bath			
6.	mop the floor			
7.	call a friend			
8.	wash the dishes			
9.	fingerpaint			
10.	go swimming			
11.	do homework			
12.	build a fire			
13.	play musical chairs			
14.	ride a bus			
15.	dress up like a clown			
16.	iron a shirt			
17.	catch a fish			
18.	wash clothes			
19.	make tacos			
20.	plant a tree			

I.E.P. Goal: The client will name items needed to perform common activities, with 90% or greater accuracy.

Task A: Naming Items Needed to Perform Activities, *continued*

List up to three things you need to do each activity below.

21. make a long-distance phone call, collect   _____   _____   _____

22. drive a car   _____   _____   _____

23. shave   _____   _____   _____

24. play baseball   _____   _____   _____

25. wash windows   _____   _____   _____

26. cut the grass   _____   _____   _____

27. knit a sweater   _____   _____   _____

28. bake cookies   _____   _____   _____

29. have a parade   _____   _____   _____

30. watch television   _____   _____   _____

31. make spaghetti   _____   _____   _____

32. change a car's oil   _____   _____   _____

33. make a pizza   _____   _____   _____

34. fix a leak in the roof   _____   _____   _____

35. buy a house   _____   _____   _____

36. send flowers to a friend   _____   _____   _____

37. find a lost dog   _____   _____   _____

38. play bingo   _____   _____   _____

39. make coffee   _____   _____   _____

40. find a job   _____   _____   _____

I.E.P. Goal: The client will name items needed to perform common activities, with 90% or greater accuracy.

Task B: Identifying Items Needed to Solve a Problem or Meet a Need

Identify all the items you would need in the following situations. The first one is done for you.

1. If you were giving a birthday party, which would you need?

   <u>cake</u>   medicine   <u>invitations</u>   <u>ice cream</u>

2. If you ripped your shirt, which would you use to repair it?

   thread   spackling   needle   zipper

3. If you wanted to make a garden, which would you need?

   hose   plants   shovel   screwdriver

4. If the heel fell off your shoe, which would you need?

   nails   tape   glue   screws

5. If your window broke, which would you need?

   saw   nail   glass   putty

6. If you wanted to chop wood for a fire, which would you use?

   hammer   ax   saw   nail

7. If you were writing a letter, which would you need?

   stamps   title   address   envelope

8. If you wanted to hang a picture, which would you need?

   glue   nail   hammer   mirror

9. If you scraped your knee, which would you need?

   toothbrush   antiseptic   cast   bandage

10. If you wanted to wrap a present, which would you need?

    candle   ribbon   tape   scissors

11. If you got a flat tire, which would you need?

    wire   jack   crowbar   drill

12. If your roof leaked, which would you use?

    tar paper   shingles   nails   hoe

I.E.P. Goal: The client will choose items necessary to solve a problem or meet a need, with 90% or greater accuracy.

Task B: Identifying Items Needed to Solve a Problem or Meet a Need, *continued*

Identify all the items you would need in the following situations.

13. If you broke your arm, which would you visit?

    physicist   pharmacist   physician   psychologist

14. If you needed new glasses, which would you visit?

    optimist   orthodontist   obstetrician   optometrist

15. If your cat were sick, which would you visit?

    veterinarian   veteran   ventriloquist   vegetarian

16. If your country wanted to negotiate with another country, which would it send?

    diploma   automat   autocraft   diplomat

17. If you wanted to know what a word meant, which would you use?

    thesaurus   dictionary   atlas   novel

18. If you had termites in your house, which would you call?

    legislator   exterminator   interior designer terminator

19. If you were writing a book, which would you need?

    stamps   crystal   topic   title

20. If you wanted to test someone's hearing, which would you use?

    thermometer   metronome   audiometer   stethescope

21. If you needed legal advice, which would you call?

    attorney   engineer   lawyer   detective

22. If you wanted to separate coffee grounds from the liquid, which would you need?

    grater   filter   stereo   strainer

23. If you had a broken string on your piano, which would you call?

    pianist   piano tuner   pessimist   guitarist

24. If you needed to add up your tax receipts, which would you need?

    calculator   percolator   odometer   adding machine

I.E.P. Goal: The client will choose items necessary to solve a problem or meet a need, with 90% or greater accuracy.

Task C: Naming Initial Steps to Perform Activities

Tell the first thing to do to begin each activity below.   The first one is done for you.

1. order a pizza to take out   *decide what kind to order* _____

2. decide what movie to see   _____

3. get ready for bed   _____

4. plant flower bulbs   _____

5. mow the lawn   _____

6. buy new shoes   _____

7. send a letter to a friend   _____

8. build a snowman   _____

9. play a baseball game   _____

10. plan a birthday party   _____

11. wash clothes   _____

12. build a fire   _____

13. fix a salad   _____

14. paint the ceiling   _____

15. wash a car   _____

16. find a lost dog   _____

17. replace a burned out light bulb   _____

18. plan a trip   _____

19. fix a cup of tea   _____

20. change a baby's diaper   _____

I.E.P. Goal: The client will identify the initial step necessary to perform common activities, with 90% or greater accuracy.

Task C: Naming Initial Steps to Perform Activities, *continued*

Tell the first thing to do to begin each activity below.

21. make Easter eggs _____

22. go to see a doctor _____

23. give a friend a recipe _____

24. clean the carpet _____

25. find a job _____

26. write a book _____

27. order tickets to a play _____

28. fix a flat tire _____

29. return an item to a store _____

30. repair a leaky inner tube _____

31. give a child medicine _____

32. fix a leaky faucet _____

33. balance your checkbook _____

34. buy new tires for a car _____

35. find a certain book in the library _____

36. stain a hardwood floor _____

37. jump start a car _____

38. reward someone for doing
    something well _____

39. obtain a mortgage loan _____

40. get up early in the morning _____

I.E.P. Goal: The client will identify the initial step necessary to perform common activities, with 90% or greater accuracy.

Task D: Identifying Information Needed to Perform Activities

List the information you need to know to do each task below. The first one is done for you.

1. call time-of-day

   the phone number

2. buy Girl Scout cookies

   _____

3. replace flashlight batteries

   _____

4. plant flower seeds

   _____

5. pick up dry cleaning

   _____

6. order a magazine subscription

   _____

7. order a pizza to take out

   _____

8. buy new shoes

   _____

9. decorate a cake

   _____

10. meet a friend for lunch

   _____

11. buy a birthday present

   _____

12. give directions to your house

   _____

I.E.P. Goal: The client will identify information needed to complete given tasks, with 90% or greater accuracy.

Task D: Identifying Information Needed to Perform Activities, *continued*

List the information you need to know to do each task below.

13. take cold medicine

_____

14. report a crime

_____

15. buy a bathrobe for someone

_____

16. make a doctor's appointment

_____

17. make dinner reservations in a restaurant

_____

18. buy a new pane of glass for a window

_____

19. rent a videotape

_____

20. report a lost dog

_____

21. wash a new shirt

_____

22. babysit for an infant

_____

23. apply for a loan

_____

24. hire someone to work for you

_____

I.E.P. Goal: The client will identify information needed to complete given tasks, with 90% or greater accuracy.

Task D: Identifying Information Needed to Perform Activities, *continued*

List the information you need to know to do each task below.

25. sew a dress

_____

26. pay a phone bill

_____

27. add oil to a car

_____

28. change a fuse

_____

29. send someone flowers for her birthday

_____

30. buy a baby gift

_____

31. decide which route to take on a trip

_____

32. buy grass seed for your lawn

_____

33. vote for a presidential candidate

_____

34. get a driver's license

_____

35. balance your checkbook

_____

36. rent an apartment

_____

I.E.P. Goal: The client will identify information needed to complete given tasks, with 90% or greater accuracy.

Task E: Giving Missing Steps in Directions

Fill in the missing step in each set of directions below. The first one is done for you.

1. plant a flower

    Dig a hole.

    <u>Put the plant in the hole.</u>

    Fill it in with dirt.

    Water the spot.

2. make chocolate milk

    Pour chocolate syrup into a glass.

    _____

    Stir with a spoon.

3. brush your teeth

    Put water on the toothbrush.

    _____

    Brush your teeth.

    Rinse out your mouth with water.

4. make Popsicles

    _____

    Put the sticks in place.

    Put the holders in the freezer.

5. make a pay phone call

    Remove the receiver.

    _____

    Dial the number.

    Have your conversation.

    Hang up the phone.

6. make a tossed salad

    Wash the lettuce.

    _____

    Chop some vegetables and add them to the lettuce.

    Add salad dressing.

    Toss the salad.

I.E.P. Goal: The client will give the missing step in a sequence of directions, with 90% or greater accuracy.

Task E: Giving Missing Steps in Directions, *continued*

Fill in the missing step in each set of directions below.

7. microwave a TV dinner   Put the TV dinner in the microwave.

_____

                               Push the start button.

                               Eat your dinner.

8. eat out at a restaurant   Call to make a reservation for dinner.

                               Get dressed appropriately.

_____

                               Order dinner and eat.

9. wrap a package   Cut paper to fit the box.

                               Fold the paper around the box.

_____

                               Tie a ribbon around the box.

10. wash clothes   Put the clothes in the washer.

                               Choose the water temperature.

_____

                               Turn on the machine.

11. make a bed   Put the bottom sheet on.

                               Put the top sheet on.

                               Put the pillows in the pillowcases.

_____

                               Put the bedspread on the bed.

12. back the car out of the driveway   Start the engine.

                               Take off the emergency brake.

                               Look behind you.

_____

                               Back out.

I.E.P. Goal: The client will give the missing step in a sequence of directions, with 90% or greater accuracy.

Fill in the missing step in each set of directions below.

13. play Monopoly

Open up the gameboard.

Choose markers.

_____

Roll the dice and move your marker.

14. Sew a button
    on a blouse

_____

Tie a knot in the thread.

Position the button on the blouse.

Sew through the button holes and the blouse.

Knot and cut the thread.

15. change a diaper

Take the wet diaper off.

Clean the diaper area.

_____

16. make pancakes

Mix the batter.

Pour the batter into the frying pan in small circles.

_____

Remove the pancakes with the spatula.

17. pay bills

Get out your checkbook and the bills.

_____

Put each check and bill stub in an envelope.

Mail the envelopes.

18. fill a wading pool

Put the wading pool in the yard.

_____

Turn on the faucet.

Turn the faucet off when the pool is full.

I.E.P. Goal: The client will give the missing step in a sequence of directions, with 90% or greater accuracy.

Task F: Predicting Inevitable Outcomes

Tell what will happen for each situation below. The first one is done for you.

1. You throw a burning match into a trash can filled with paper.

   The paper will catch on fire.

2. You drop an egg carton.

   _____

3. You let go of a helium-filled balloon.

   _____

4. You cook an egg in boiling water for ten minutes.

   _____

5. You leave an ice cream carton on the kitchen counter for half an hour.

   _____

6. You put a letter in the mailbox without putting a stamp on it first.

   _____

7. You fill a glass to the rim with water and then add two ice cubes.

   _____

8. You put loose change in a pocket with a hole in it.

   _____

9. You take a casserole out of the oven without using pot holders.

   _____

10. You get a nail stuck in your bicycle tire.

    _____

11. You don't ever study or go to class.

    _____

12. You wash a pair of jeans with a tissue in the pocket.

    _____

I.E.P. Goal: The client will predict inevitable outcomes of situations, with 90% or greater accuracy.

Task F: Predicting Inevitable Outcomes, *continued*

Tell what will happen for each situation below.

13. You are two hours late to work every day.

_____

14. You leave a lamp in the living room on all the time.

_____

15. You turn on the broiler instead of the oven when baking a cake.

_____

16. A car runs a stop sign while a truck is in the intersection.

_____

17. The temperature drops to 20 degrees after a rainstorm.

_____

18. You put cut flowers in a vase without any water.

_____

19. You try to visit a foreign country without a passport.

_____

20. You take a photograph before removing the lens cover from the camera.

_____

21. You drive the wrong way on a one-way street.

_____

22. You substitute clay for cement when building a brick wall.

_____

23. You get more votes than your competition for the office of treasurer.

_____

24. You put lyrics and a tune together.

_____

I.E.P. Goal: The client will predict inevitable outcomes of situations, with 90% or greater accuracy.

Task G: Determining the Relative Difficulty of Related Activities

Decide which activity in each pair is easier to do. Then, tell why. The first one is done for you.

1. riding a bicycle   riding a tricycle

   tricycle - It's easier to balance.

2. buying a sweater   making a sweater

3. jumping over a log   jumping over a stick

4. dialing the telephone   answering the telephone

5. folding a blanket   folding a towel

6. cutting a twig   sawing down a tree

7. doing a chore   painting a house

8. getting a haircut   giving a haircut

9. driving a car   driving a tractor

10. lighting a gas lantern   lighting a lamp

11. playing tennis   playing catch

12. making ice   making ice cream

I.E.P. Goal: The client will determine which of two related activities is easier to perform, with 90% or greater accuracy.

Task G: Determining the Relative Difficulty of Related Activities, *continued*

Decide which activity in each pair is easier to do. Then, tell why.

13. making instant coffee   making brewed coffee

_____

14. putting on glasses   putting on contact lenses

_____

15. painting a ceiling   painting a wall

_____

16. adding numbers   dividing numbers

_____

17. skiing downhill   skiing cross country

_____

18. making toast   making bread

_____

19. operating a motorboat   operating a sailboat

_____

20. dancing a ballet   dancing a waltz

_____

21. adding fractions   adding whole numbers

_____

22. reading a magazine   reading a novel

_____

23. playing a guitar   playing a harmonica

_____

24. making a movie   watching a video tape

_____

I.E.P. Goal: The client will determine which of two related activities is easier to perform, with 90% or greater accuracy.

Task H: Identifying the Presence or Absence of a Problem

Tell whether each statement describes a problem or not. If it describes a problem, tell why. The first one is done for you.

1. Mrs. Jeffries forgot to take her cake out of the oven.

   (yes) no   _Her cake burned._ _____

2. Nancy was thirsty, so her mom got her a drink.

   yes   no   _____

3. Mark licked his ice cream cone and the top scoop slipped off.

   yes   no   _____

4. Mom and Dad got paid at work today. They put the money in the bank.

   yes   no   _____

5. Melissa's balloon began to hiss.

   yes   no   _____

6. Suddenly, the teapot began to make a loud whistling noise.

   yes   no   _____

7. Jack ate at a restaurant, but left his wallet at home.

   yes   no   _____

8. Sarah caught the bus early in the morning.

   yes   no   _____

9. Joshua kicked the football and when John caught it, it was flat.

   yes   no   _____

10. I was sitting on my bed reading when it began raining on my head.

    yes   no   _____

11. The sun came out and the birds began to sing.

    yes   no   _____

12. Mom left the iron on while she went shopping.

    yes   no   _____

I.E.P. Goal: The client will determine the presence or absence of a problem in a given situation, with 90% or greater accuracy.

Task H: Identifying the Presence or Absence of a Problem, *continued*

Tell whether each statement describes a problem or not. If it describes a problem, tell why.

13. We stopped the car when we came to a red traffic light.

    yes   no   _____

14. The neighborhood dogs played in the garbage cans we left out.

    yes   no   _____

15. The lamp suddenly went off while Phil was reading Monday evening.

    yes   no   _____

16. The acrobat flipped three times in the air before grabbing the trapeze.

    yes   no   _____

17. The lantern helped us to see outside when we were camping.

    yes   no   _____

18. Evan's temperature was 102° and he felt weak.

    yes   no   _____

19. The car's gas gauge was on E.

    yes   no   _____

20. The ocean liner swayed from side to side as the waves rose and fell.

    yes   no   _____

21. Jan and Paul are ice skating on thin ice.

    yes   no   _____

22. Carla went outside in her bathrobe to get the mail and the door locked behind her.

    yes   no   _____

23. When George went to the doctor's office, she removed his stitches.

    yes   no   _____

24. The car veered to the right when the steering wheel was turned clockwise.

    yes   no   _____

I.E.P. Goal: The client will determine the presence or absence of a problem in a given situation, with 90% or greater accuracy.

Task I: Identifying the Problem

Read each situation below. Then, tell what the problem is. The first one is done for you.

1. Ted wants to take his dog for a walk, but the dog only has a collar.

   He needs a leash.

2. Mary wants to brush her teeth. She can only find the toothpaste.

   _____

3. Stuart's jacket zipper wouldn't move up or down.

   _____

4. Joe's ice cream was melted when he took it out of the freezer.

   _____

5. While Kathy was taking a test, her pencil broke.

   _____

6. You are building a fire. You have only wood, newspaper and kindling.

   _____

7. The milk smelled bad when Jerry poured it on his cereal.

   _____

8. Michael turned on the TV. He could only hear the characters talking.

   _____

9. You tried on some tight jeans at the store. When you leaned over, you heard a strange sound.

   _____

10. Leah went to catch the bus after school, but no one was there.

    _____

11. Jack wrote on the last page of his notebook.

    _____

12. Ken was going for a walk. His shoe got stuck on the sidewalk.

    _____

I.E.P. Goal: The client will be able to identify the nature of problems in situations, with 90% or greater accuracy.

Read each situation below. Then, tell what the problem is.

13. Jeremy hit the baseball with his new bat in his backyard. Suddenly, he heard a crash and someone shouting.

_____

14. A friend gave you a pair of shoes that hurt when you put them on.

_____

15. Stephen put his key in the front door lock, but the key wouldn't turn.

_____

16. Monica took a shower. She was so cold she trembled when she got out.

_____

17. Maureen was cooking pasta. Suddenly, she heard a loud hissing sound.

_____

18. Luke heard a buzzing sound when he made a phone call.

_____

19. When I plugged in the iron, the air conditioner and the lights went off.

_____

20. Tony took the stopper out of the sink, but the water didn't run out.

_____

21. When the dentist looked at your X-rays, he saw two dark spots.

_____

22. Lisa drove to a friend's house. While she was there, she lost one of her contact lenses.

_____

23. Val, Rose and Linda wanted to play bridge, but no one else was home.

_____

I.E.P. Goal: The client will be able to identify the nature of problems in situations, with 90% or greater accuracy.

Task J: Solving a Problem — Choice of Two Solutions

Choose the appropriate solution to each problem below. The first one is done for you.

1. Lou is walking to the movie theater. He has to cross a busy street alone. He should _____.

   (a.) look both ways and cross with the light at the corner
   b. run across the street to the theater

2. When Mary got off the school bus, she realized she left her sweater in her classroom. She should _____.

   a. walk back to school to get her sweater
   b. pick up her sweater the next day at school

3. John was getting dressed for an important meeting. He couldn't find two socks that matched. He should _____.

   a. wear one navy sock and one black sock
   b. wear a pair of matched sweat socks

4. When Margaret took some meat out of the freezer, she realized it was not frozen. She should _____.

   a. throw out the meat and the other items that may be spoiled
   b. be glad the meat was already thawed and cook it for dinner

5. Jennifer was babysitting late one evening when someone knocked at the door. She should _____.

   a. open the door and find out who is there and what he needs
   b. ask through the door who it is

6. David was cutting down a tree when it fell on a power line. He should _____.

   a. try to move the tree off the power line without damaging the wire
   b. call the power company for some help

7. Jane heard a bubbling sound and realized her washing machine was overflowing. She should _____.

   a. turn off the machine, clean up the water and call a repair service
   b. wait until the washer finishes the cycle before turning it off

8. Mary Ann had a flat tire on her way home. She should _____.

   a. keep driving until she gets home and then change the tire
   b. pull over immediately and either change her tire or ask someone for help

9. Janet was typing a paper for school and made several typing errors. She should _____.

   a. type over each error with the correct letter or number
   b. use white-out or a correcting ribbon to correct the errors

I.E.P. Goal: The client will choose the appropriate solution for given situations, with 90% or greater accuracy.

Task J: Solving a Problem — Choice of Two Solutions, *continued*

Choose the appropriate solution to each problem below.

10. Someone broke into Ian's car, shattering one of the windows. Rain is in the forecast. Ian should _____.

    a. cover the window with plastic until he can have the glass replaced
    b. park his car under a tree, hoping to shield it from the rain

11. Harry was tying his hiking boot when one of his laces broke in half. He should _____.

    a. piece the lace together until he can buy another one
    b. take the lace out and buy a new one

12. A raccoon near the creek bit Ben on the thumb. Ben should _____.

    a. not tell anyone because it was just a small bite
    b. tell his parents because he might need to see a doctor

13. Angela was vacuuming her rug when dust and dirt suddenly came flying out of the hose. She should _____.

    a. unplug the vacuum and empty the bag
    b. finish vacuuming the room

14. Dan was having company for dinner. As he took the roast out of the pan, the roast fell on the kitchen floor. Dan should _____.

    a. throw the roast away and take his guests out to dinner
    b. rinse off the roast and serve it, keeping the accident a secret

15. Bob's car was making a funny clicking noise as he drove to the store. He should _____.

    a. turn on the car radio so he can't hear the noise
    b. pull into a service station and ask someone to check the car

16. Joe got a new retainer from his orthodontist. At school, he accidentally threw it in the trash after lunch. He should _____.

    a. tell his parents what happened so they can get him a new retainer
    b. wear his old retainer and pretend it is the new one

17. Dianne was baking cookies for her class. When she opened the flour canister, she found some bugs in it. She should _____.

    a. go to the store and buy a new bag of flour
    b. carefully spoon out the bugs, being sure none get in the batter

18. Mr. King left his meeting to sharpen his pencil. When he came back, someone was sitting in his seat. He should _____.

    a. shove the other person out of his seat and sit down again
    b. pick up his belongings and move to another seat

I.E.P Goal: The client will choose the appropriate solution for given situations, with 90% or greater accuracy.

Critical Thinking
Task J: Solving a Problem — Choice of Two Solutions, *continued*

Choose the appropriate solution to each problem below.

19. Jeff was cooking spaghetti noodles when he noticed that the pot was boiling over. He should _____.

    a. turn the burner down and cook the spaghetti more slowly
    b. let the spaghetti keep boiling so that it will eventually lose enough water that it won't overflow

20. Penelope hit another car in the parking lot when she was leaving her parking space. She should _____.

    a. just keep driving because the other driver probably wouldn't mind
    b. leave a note on the car she hit giving her name, address and phone number so the driver can contact her about fixing the damage

21. While Peggy was driving on the highway, she saw a man parked beside the road with his car hood raised. She should _____.

    a. go to the next rest stop and call the highway patrol to help the man
    b. honk the horn of her car and wave at him

22. Evelyn was getting dressed and the zipper on the back of her dress got stuck halfway up. She was home alone. She should _____.

    a. use scissors to take the side seam out of her dress so she can take it off
    b. wear a sweater to work and ask someone to help her free the zipper

23. Ben and Cathy went to the movies, but they couldn't find two seats together. They should _____.

    a. ask for their money back and go home
    b. ask someone sitting between two empty seats to move over one seat

24. Eric and his dad were fishing in a boat. Eric cut his finger on a bait knife and it wouldn't stop bleeding. He should _____.

    a. hold his hand up and press it with a clean cloth or his shirt until they can get to a doctor
    b. dangle his finger in the cold water to stop the bleeding

25. Chuck's four-year-old sister was playing with the new watch he got for his birthday and she broke it. Chuck should _____.

    a. ask his mom or dad to have the watch repaired
    b. make his sister pay for a new watch

26. Brian found an old wallet while he was walking along the beach. There were credit cards inside, but no address and no money. He should _____.

    a. throw the wallet away because it's old and ragged
    b. take the wallet to the police so they can locate the owner

I.E.P Goal: The client will choose the appropriate solution for given situations, with 90% or greater accuracy.

Task K: Completing Open-Ended Statements

Finish each statement. The first one is done for you.

1. The fence was too high to climb over, so Linda

   <u>went through the gate.</u>

2. Nelson's bicycle wheels squeaked, so he

   _____

3. Dana was always late for work, so she

   _____

4. Max became very tired and out of breath while doing his chores, so he

   _____

5. Fred had a terrible headache, so he

   _____

6. The phone line went dead while Paul was calling his mother, so he

   _____

7. Mike's basketball was flat, so he

   _____

8. Ollie didn't feel well. To see if he was sick, he

   _____

9. Gail's tape recorder was playing much too loudly, so she

   _____

10. Marjorie's flashlight grew weaker and weaker. Finally, the light was gone. She

    _____

11. When Lisa was getting dressed, the button popped off her skirt. She

    _____

12. George was in an elevator when suddenly it stopped between floors. He
    waited a minute for it to move and when it didn't, he

    _____

I.E.P. Goal: The client will complete open-ended problem or solution statements, with 90% or greater accuracy.

Task K: Completing Open-Ended Statements, *continued*

Finish each statement.

13. Elaine's plants were drooping and the soil was dry, so she

14. David's sister accused him of taking her watch, but she found it in her room. She decided she should

15. Rebecca had nothing to wear to the prom, so she

16. Jamie saw a detour sign while she was riding her bike, so she

17. Theresa wanted hot tea, so she put water in the pot and

18. The last four pages of Donna's mystery novel were missing, so she

19. Fred's uncle gave him one hundred dollars for graduation. Fred didn't want to loose the money or spend it on things he didn't need, so he

20. Sharon wanted to pay for a new skirt at the store. She had no cash and she was over her limit on her credit card, so she

21. Jane wanted to wash her hair while she was taking a shower, but she realized there was no shampoo in the shower. She

22. Phyllis was getting dressed for a party. She didn't know whether the party was formal or casual, so she

23. Jack and Emily's car was covered with snow one morning, so they

I.E.P. Goal: The client will complete open-ended problem or solution statements, with 90% or greater accuracy.

Task L: Solving Situational Problems

Answer the question to tell ways to solve each problem. The first one is done for you.

1. Alan is painting a picture. He runs out of green paint just as he is beginning to paint the trees. What could he do?

   mix blue and yellow paint

2. Laura is baking a cake. She needs a quarter of a cup more sugar. What could she do?

   _____

3. Nancy is babysitting for three children. There are four Popsicles in the freezer. She gives each child a Popsicle. One child finishes his and wants another Popsicle. The other children also want the other Popsicle. What could Nancy do?

   _____

4. A new family is moving into the house next door. They are having difficulty fitting the couch through the front door. What could they do?

   _____

5. Linda has chewing gum in her hair. What could her mother do to get it out?

   _____

6. Mr. Simmons is locked out of his house. What could he do?

   _____

7. Jan's friend brought a Christmas gift over to her house. Jan doesn't have a gift for her. What could Jan do?

   _____

8. The Andersons are going on vacation. All three children want to sit by the window in the car. What could be done so the children don't fight?

   _____

9. Pam is getting ready for work when the schools close because of snow. Pam has a young child, and she needs to get to work. What could she do?

   _____

10. Paul was mowing his lawn when it suddenly began to drizzle. He had half the yard done. What could he do?

   _____

I.E.P. Goal: When presented with problem situations, the client will generate possible solutions, with 90% or greater accuracy.

Task L: Solving Situational Problems, *continued*

Answer the question to tell ways to solve each problem.

11. Madge was speaking with her father-in-law on the telephone when she was suddenly cut off. What could she do?

_____

12. Mom was drying her laundry. After two complete drying cycles, her clothes were still soaking wet. What could she do?

_____

13. Gary was eating French fries and ran out of ketchup. What could he do?

_____

14. David arrived at school without his lunchbox. What could he do?

_____

15. Bea was driving to her cousin's house. She got lost. What could Bea do?

_____

16. Carolyn was in a school play. Suddenly, she forgot her lines. What could she do?

_____

17. Steven was riding his horse out in the fields when the horse injured its foot. What could he do?

_____

18. Jan discovered she was wearing one black shoe and one blue one. What could she do?

_____

19. John was driving on a highway when his car broke down. He was a half a mile from the next exit. What could he do?

_____

20. Alex and Sherry went to a concert. When they found their assigned seats, two people were sitting in them. What could Alex and Sherry do?

_____

I.E.P. Goal: When presented with problem situations, the client will generate possible solutions, with 90% or greater accuracy.

Critical Thinking
Task M: Choosing the Best Available Solution to a Problem

Think of a solution for each problem below. The first one is done for you.

1. You are at work and the hem rips out of your dress. You don't have a needle and thread. What could you do?

   Use safety pins or tape to hold up the hem.

2. Your Christmas tree stand breaks while you try to put up the tree. All the stores are closed. What could you do?

   _____

3. Jack's dog needs to go for a walk, but the leash is missing. Jack doesn't have any rope. What could he do?

   _____

4. You'd like an egg for breakfast, but you don't have any butter, margarine, or shortening. What could you do?

   _____

5. You are getting ready to paint a room, but you can't find a paint stirrer. You look in your desk for an old ruler, but you don't have one. What could you do?

   _____

6. Chris needs to take some cookies out of the oven, but she can't find any pot holders or kitchen towels. What could she do?

   _____

7. You are wrapping a birthday gift and you run out of clear tape. You decide to use masking tape, but you can't find any. What could you do?

   _____

8. You need to get in touch with a friend right away, but you don't have a telephone. What else could you do?

   _____

9. Paula needs to fasten some papers together. She doesn't have any staples. She looks for some paper clips but can't find any. What else could she do?

   _____

I.E.P. Goal: The client will give an alternate solution to a problem when the ideal solution is not possible, with 90% accuracy.

Task M: Choosing the Best Available Solution to a Problem, *continued*

Think of a solution for each problem below.

10. You are home one evening alone when the electricity suddenly goes off. You can't find the candles or the flashlights. What else could you do?

_____

11. Kathy is braiding her daughter's hair. She has no rubber bands. She tries to fasten the braids with barrettes, but the hair is too thick. What could Kathy do?

_____

12. You have a bad cold and you can't breathe through your nose. You don't have any nasal spray or a vaporizer in the house. What else could you do?

_____

13. You want to give your son a haircut. You have no hair clippers and you can't find your scissors. What else could you do?

_____

14. You broke a glass on the kitchen floor. Your vacuum cleaner is not working properly and you can't find a broom. What else could you do?

_____

15. You want to find a new job. You don't have a home phone and you don't want prospective employers to call you at work. What else could you do?

_____

16. Your neck aches. Your electric heating pad is broken and you lost your hot water bottle when you moved. What else could you do?

_____

17. You locked your keys in the car. You don't have another set and no locksmith is available. What else could you do?

_____

18. You are driving in town and realize you don't know where you are. You don't have a map and there is no one around to ask. What else could you do?

_____

I.E.P. Goal: The client will give an alternate solution to a problem when the ideal solution is not possible, with 90% or greater accuracy.

Task M: Choosing the Best Available Solution to a Problem, *continued*

Think of a solution for each problem below.

19. You need to wake up at 7 A.M. to leave for a trip. Your power goes off at 9 P.M., and you don't have a travel alarm. What could you do?

_____

20. An ocean wave hits Ted and breaks the bag he's using to collect shells. He can't find a box or another bag to carry the shells. What should he do?

_____

21. Stan's only pencil breaks while he's doing his homework. His pencil sharpener is jammed, and his pens are out of ink. What else could he use?

_____

22. Kay put coins in the parking meter, but nothing happened when she turned the handle. There aren't any other parking spaces. What could she do?

_____

23. The Edwards want to cook hamburgers on their camping cookstove, but the grill is missing. They have no aluminum foil. What could they do?

_____

24. You're painting your bedroom and you don't have any dropcloths. No stores are open because it's late at night. What could you do?

_____

25. You want to open a corked bottle, but you don't have a corkscrew. What could you do?

_____

26. You want to plant some bulbs. The ground is too hard to use your hands to dig, and you don't have a trowel. What could you do?

_____

27. You are playing checkers with a friend. There aren't enough red checkers, and you have no red poker chips. What could you do?

_____

I.E.P. Goal: The client will give an alternate solution to a problem when the ideal solution is not possible, with 90% or greater accuracy.

Task N: Giving Instructions to Solve a Problem

Identify and order the steps to solve each problem below. The first one is done for you.

1. Alice is at the park. She needs to call both her mom and her boyfriend to let them know she will be late getting home. She only has enough change for one phone call. What should she do?

   a. *Go to the payphone and call her boyfriend.*

   b. *Ask him to call her mom and give her the message.*

2. You are having a picnic. Suddenly the wind gusts, scattering paper plates and napkins everywhere. What should you do?

3. Adam and Don's favorite television shows are on at the same time. The family only has one TV and each boy wants to watch his show. What should the family do?

4. Marsha comes home from work and discovers her bracelet is missing. What should she do?

5. Steven drives to the exit of the parking garage and finds he doesn't have enough money in his wallet to pay the fee. What should Steven do?

6. Evelyn is sitting in the boat and her keys fall over the side into the lake. What should Evelyn do?

7. You are making popcorn on the stove. You can smell it burning on the bottom before it is done popping. What should you do?

8. Tim, Randy, and Ted are best friends. They all decided to buy the same style and color of soccer shoes. After practice, they took off their shoes and threw them together in a pile. When it was time to go home, they didn't know which pair of shoes each boy should take. What should they do?

9. Jane was filling the kitchen sink to wash dishes when she heard a loud crash outside. She went to see what happened and when she returned, water was overflowing onto the kitchen floor. What should Jane do?

10. You are trying to blow up a beach ball, but it doesn't get any bigger as you try to inflate it. What should you do?

11. Your hair gets tangled in your ring while you are brushing it. What should you do?

12. You switch on the furnace in your house, but nothing happens. What should you do?

13. While you are cutting the grass, the mower suddenly stops. What should you do?

14. The needle on your sewing machine breaks while you are sewing. What should you do?

I.E.P. Goal: The client will identify appropriate sequential steps to solve a problem, with 90% or greater accuracy.

Task N: Giving Instructions to Solve a Problem, *continued*

Identify and order the steps to solve each problem below.

15. Your car gets a flat tire while you are driving on a country road. What should you do?

16. Marion is giving her two year old son a bath when she hears a crash from her five year old's bedroom. She hears frantic cries from the room. What should Marion do?

17. While taking her daughter, Laura, to a birthday party, Penny realizes she has forgotten to bring the child's present. They are less than a block from the birthday child's house. What should Laura do?

18. Joan is hurrying to dress for a job interview. She looks at her watch and realizes it stopped hours ago. She doesn't know what time it is, and she needs to use her watch during the job interview. What should she do?

19. Ben bought a pair of boots to wear on his mountain hike next weekend. He wore them home from the store to break them in and realized they rubbed terribly on the side of his big toe. What should Ben do?

20. Sarah was at a friend's party. Suddenly, Jack spilled his juice all over her red dress. What should Sarah do?

21. Mr. White was working out at the gym one afternoon. He had been exercising for over an hour. While riding the exercise bicycle, he began to get dizzy and felt faint. What should he do?

22. Janet wants to go see a movie. She wants to ask a friend to go with her, but she doesn't know which movies are in town, how much they cost, or what time they start. What should Janet do?

23. Marsha's mother is very ill and needs help immediately. Marsha lives over a thousand miles away from her mom, and her car isn't reliable enough for a long trip. What should Marsha do?

24. Mr. McArthur's cows are wandering out on the main road. What should he do?

25. Mark and Jeff were canoeing down the lake when a sudden wave from a large powerboat flipped them into the water. What should they do?

26. Margaret wants to write a dear friend a note, but she has run out of writing paper with matching envelopes. What should she do?

I.E.P. Goal: The client will identify appropriate sequential steps to solve a problem, with 90% or greater accuracy.

Task O: Determining Why a Solution Is Incorrect

For each item below, tell why the given solution will not work. The first one is done for you.

1. I had a hole in my sock, so I safety-pinned it shut.

   The pin will dig in your foot when you put your shoe on.

2. I broke the lens in my glasses, so I borrowed my sister's pair.

   _____

3. I forgot to take my medicine this morning, so I'll take twice as much at lunch.

   _____

4. The chicken was supposed to bake at 350° for an hour. I forgot to turn on the oven, so I'll bake the chicken at 450° for forty minutes.

   _____

5. I ran out of laundry detergent, so I used a cup of dishwashing liquid instead.

   _____

6. Bob didn't have a stamp to mail his letter, so he wrote C.O.D. on it and dropped it in the mailbox.

   _____

7. Rita didn't have a quarter for the pay phone, so she deposited two dimes instead.

   _____

8. Carla was making a dress for herself and needed to measure her waist. She couldn't find the tape measure, so she used a ruler instead.

   _____

9. I couldn't find the stopper to the bathtub, so I plugged up the drain with a washcloth when I took a bath.

   _____

10. Ann didn't have enough yarn to knit the second sleeve of her sweater, so she left off the last five rows.

    _____

I.E.P. Goal: The client will determine why given solutions to common problems are incorrect, with 90% or greater accuracy.

Task O: Determining Why a Solution Is Incorrect, *continued*

For each item below, tell why the given solution will not work.

11. Brent couldn't remember the combination to his lock, so he used a key instead.

_____

12. Uncle Joe couldn't find a bucket, so he mixed the cement in the laundry basket.

_____

13. Albert's necktie was too short, so he made a bigger knot in it.

_____

14. Dave ran out of wax for his surfboard, so he used vegetable oil instead.

_____

15. Brenda didn't have a spatula, so she used a fork to turn her fried egg over.

_____

16. Adam was walking down a country road one evening and tripped and hurt his ankle badly. He began to yell for a doctor.

_____

17. Dean sat on a lopsided chair. He realized one of the four legs was shorter than the others, so he cut off one of the other chair legs.

_____

18. Otto's car was nearly out of gas. Otto took the car to the repair shop and got a tune-up to make the car run more economically.

_____

19. Jean was ten minutes late to the bus stop and realized that she had missed her bus to work. When the next bus came along, she hopped aboard.

_____

20. Our TV picture was very light and fuzzy, so we turned up the brightness control.

_____

I.E.P. Goal: The client will determine why given solutions to common problems are incorrect, with 90% or greater accuracy.

Task P: Identifying Possible Causes of a Given Problem

Identify all the possible causes for each situation below. The first one is done for you.

1. You go to take a shower and there is no hot water.

    (a) The hot water heater is broken.
    (b) Several people just took showers before you.
    c. The temperature in the bathroom is too low.
    (d) The hot water pipe burst.

2. The car coasts to a stop and the engine dies.

    a. You have a flat tire.
    b. You are out of gas.
    c. The water pump is broken.
    d. The battery is dead.
    e. There is a hole in the muffler.

3. You go to make a telephone call and the line is dead.

    a. The phone is unplugged.
    b. The power lines are down.
    c. The electricity is off.
    d. You didn't pay your phone bill.
    e. Someone is trying to call you at the same time.

4. You go to a friend's house for dinner. No one answers the door.

    a. She is not at home.
    b. The doorbell is broken.
    c. It is a holiday.
    d. You are at the wrong house.
    e. You are wearing the wrong clothing.
    f. She is in the back yard.

5. You turn on the television, but there is no picture.

    a. It is unplugged.
    b. It is broken.
    c. It has been left on too long.
    d. The power is off.
    e. The volume is not turned up.
    f. Someone is watching television in the next room.

6. You oversleep because the alarm clock doesn't ring.

    a. You forgot to set it.
    b. It is broken.
    c. It is too cold in the room.
    d. The electricity went off during the night.
    e. It isn't plugged in.

I.E.P. Goal: The client will determine possible causes for given problems, with 90% or greater accuracy.

Task P: Identifying Possible Causes of a Given Problem, *continued*

Identify all the possible causes for each situation below.

7. You turn down a city street, but the street is blocked off.

   a. The water main is broken.
   b. Workers are repairing the street.
   c. It is an election day.
   d. A parade is about to begin.
   e. Rain is coming.
   f. An accident just happened.

8. You wake up and look out your window. The grass is all wet.

   a. It rained during the night.
   b. There is dew on the grass.
   c. It snowed during the night.
   d. Someone drove a car through the yard.
   e. A water pipe under the house is leaking.
   f. You are having a drought.

9. You turn on the TV to watch the 11 P.M. news, but a movie is on.

   a. The movie has run late.
   b. There has been a presidential press conference.
   c. It is Saturday night.
   d. Your clock is wrong.
   e. You have the wrong channel on.
   f. The news has been cancelled due to poor ratings.

10. You are hiking. Suddenly, you feel a pain in your foot.

    a. You have a rock in your shoe.
    b. You twisted your foot while walking.
    c. The altitude is too high.
    d. There is a hole in the bottom of your shoe.
    e. You have a blister on your foot.
    f. You ate too much for lunch.

11. Your house key won't turn in the lock of your front door.

    a. It is the wrong key.
    b. The lock is broken.
    c. The key is broken.
    d. It is the wrong house.
    e. The key is metal.

12. When Carla stopped to pick up her laundry at the cleaners, they were unable to give it to her.

    a. Carla bought a new suit on Saturday.
    b. Carla came before the time the cleaners promised to have it ready.
    c. Carla got married the day before.
    d. Carla went to the wrong cleaners.
    e. Carla's husband picked the laundry up an hour earlier.

I.E.P. Goal: The client will determine possible causes for given problems, with 90% or greater accuracy.

Task P: Identifying Possible Causes of a Given Problem, *continued*

Identify all the possible causes for each situation below.

13. Debbie's babysitter called and said she couldn't babysit next week.

    a. The babysitter has the flu and needs to stay home in bed.
    b. The babysitter bought new furniture for her den.
    c. The babysitter's husband was going to be out of town.
    d. The babysitter was going on vacation.
    e. The babysitter needed to help a neighbor with her garden.

14. Bill wanted to charge an expensive ring on his credit card, but he was told that he must pay cash for the ring.

    a. The store only accepts cash.
    b. Bill had exceeded his credit limit on his credit card.
    c. Bill did not have his credit card or account number with him.
    d. Bill was very upset about his mother being ill.
    e. Bill's wife was going to pay for the ring.

15. One day at preschool, Sarah didn't eat her snack.

    a. Sarah didn't want what they were having that day for snack.
    b. The preschool didn't have enough food.
    c. The preschool didn't have snacks that day due to a field trip.
    d. Sarah came to preschool after snack was over.
    e. Sarah will be going to elementary school next year.

16. Grant couldn't find a shirt in his closet.

    a. Grant wears a size 16 shirt.
    b. Grant put his pants, socks, and shoes on first.
    c. Grant forgot to pick up his laundry.
    d. Grant had hung his shirts in another closet.
    e. Grant forgot to take his shirts to the cleaners.

17. Linda invited her in-laws to a formal dinner party, but they declined her invitation.

    a. Linda's in-laws are uncomfortable at fancy affairs.
    b. Linda's in-laws are angry with her over an argument earlier in the week.
    c. Linda's children are teenagers.
    d. Linda's in-laws were going on vacation that week.
    e. Linda invited them weeks in advance.

18. When Mary Jo arrived home on her birthday, she had no birthday cards in her mailbox.
    a. No one remembered her birthday.
    b. Mary Jo loves birthday cards.
    c. Mary Jo's husband picked up the mail earlier when he got home.
    d. Mary Jo was thirty years old.
    e. It was a holiday and the mail wasn't delivered that day.

I.E.P. Goal: The client will determine possible causes for given problems, with 90% or greater accuracy.

Task P: Identifying Possible Causes of a Given Problem, *continued*

Identify all the possible causes for each situation below.

19. When Maria got Christopher up from his nap, she noticed his sheet was wet.

    a. Christopher wore a new sleeper to bed.
    b. Christopher's diaper leaked.
    c. Christopher was so hot, he perspired while he slept.
    d. Christopher was teething and was drooling a great deal.
    e. Christopher's father gave him a bath before his nap.

20. The door was locked when Jeremy got to the city library.

    a. It was Sunday morning and the library was closed.
    b. Jeremy tried to enter through the wrong door.
    c. Jeremy forgot to ring the doorbell.
    d. The library was closed for repairs and redecorating.
    e. It was past closing time.

21. Matt planted grass seed in April, but his yard was just dirt by late May.

    a. Matt likes dirt better than grass.
    b. Matt didn't sow enough seed.
    c. Matt didn't water the yard enough after the seed was planted.
    d. A late winter storm damaged the grass seed.
    e. Matt likes to work in his yard.

22. Jim's friend, Al, wasn't in school on Friday.

    a. Al was captain of the football team.
    b. Al was sick that day.
    c. Al's family went away on a long weekend trip.
    d. Friday was a school holiday.
    e. Al missed the bus.

23. After Stuart read the Sunday paper, he realized he hadn't seen the comics section.

    a. The comics were stuck to another section.
    b. The comics were in color.
    c. The comics were missing from the paper.
    d. The comics fell where Stuart couldn't see them.
    e. The comics weren't very funny.

24. The carpet just inside your front door was wet when you came home after a rainstorm.

    a. The room was just vacuumed.
    b. The roof leaks.
    c. The door window was left open.
    d. The furniture had been polished.
    e. Your pet wet the rug.

I.E.P. Goal: The client will determine possible causes for given problems, with 90% or greater accuracy.

Task Q: Avoiding Problems

For each situation below, decide how the problem could have been avoided. The first one is done for you.

1. Valerie wanted to feed her dog. She went to the cupboard, but there was no dog food left. Valerie should have _____.

   <u>bought some more when she noticed it was getting low</u>

2. Josh bought a quart of milk, some bread and a dozen eggs at the store. When Josh got home, three of the eggs were cracked. Josh should have _____.

3. Jamie had a luncheon date with her boyfriend, Ned, at noon. Because of the heavy lunch hour traffic, she was one hour late. Ned was furious. Jamie should have _____.

4. Greg got an F on his geography test. Rather than have his parents furious with him over this poor grade, he changed the letter to make his grade look like a B. Noticing the different color inks on Greg's paper, his mother confronted him about rewriting his grade. Greg should have _____.

5. Nola had just finished polishing her nails when she decided to call a friend for a chat while they dried. She dialed the number and spoke to her friend for about ten minutes. Later, Nola noticed her nails had chipped and there were smeared spots on several fingers. Nola should have _____.

6. Carl wrote a check to pay for new shirts, but the check bounced. Carl should have _____.

7. Daniel invited Carol to a dinner theater Saturday night for a play and a late supper. They arrived at the theater on time, but there were no seats left. Daniel should have _____.

I.E.P. Goal: The client will tell what could have been done to avoid problem situations, with 90% or greater accuracy.

Task Q: Avoiding Problems, *continued*

For each situation below, decide how the problem could have been avoided.

8. When Fred and Rita came home from vacation, their newspapers were piled up on their front porch and mail was spilling out of their mailbox. They should have _____.

_____

9. Mark took his car to the service shop for repairs on the way to work Thursday. At five o'clock, he called the repair person to make arrangements to pick up the car. He was told the car wouldn't be ready until Friday afternoon. Now, Mark has no transportation to and from work. He should have _____.

_____

10. On Monday, Grace's three year old son had a temperature of 103° and a bad cold. On Tuesday, his temperature was 101° and Grace took him with her to go shopping for several hours. When they got home, his temperature was 104°. Grace should have _____.

_____

11. Anna saw a pair of shoes she really liked in a department store. She bought them and took them home. When she tried them on, they were too tight. Anna should have _____.

_____

12. Marge told her neighbor she would babysit for her on Friday night. Later, she realized Friday night was also the big football game she had promised to go to with her friends. Marge should have _____.

_____

13. Mary was in a hurry to get home from the airport. She took a blue suitcase off the luggage carousel and hurried home. When she got home, she realized the suitcase wasn't hers. Mary should have _____.

_____

14. Ben bought a sweater on sale as a birthday gift for his sister. The sweater was too small for her, so she took it back to the store. The store wouldn't exchange the sweater because it had been on sale. Ben should have _____.

_____

I.E.P. Goal: The client will tell what could have been done to avoid problem situations, with 90% or greater accuracy.

Task Q: Avoiding Problems, *continued*

For each situation below, decide how the problem could have been avoided.

15. Bill put the trash out Monday evening so it could be picked up Tuesday morning. During the night, some dogs tipped the cans over and made a mess of all the garbage. Bill should have _____.

_____

16. Larry made an impressive sales presentation at 10:00. When he got back to his office, an angry client informed him he had been waiting for over an hour for the meeting they had scheduled at 10:00 that morning. Larry should have _____.

_____

17. Ms. Henderson had gotten poor performance reviews from her supervisors for over two years. One day, she was told to take her belongings and leave because her services were no longer required by the business. She should have _____.

_____

18. Jody wanted to lighten her hair color slightly. After she colored, washed and dried her hair, she was upset to find it was almost white. Jody should have _____.

_____

19. Carter's aunt gave him a shirt he didn't like for his birthday. He thanked her for the shirt, then exchanged it at the store for a record album. His aunt is coming to visit and wants to see him wearing the new shirt. Carter should have _____.

_____

20. We sat in the sun while we watched the game. Our arms and faces got sunburned. We should have _____.

_____

21. When Brad got out his Monopoly game, he was disappointed to find one die missing and most of the cards bent from the way the game had been put away. Brad should have _____.

_____

I.E.P. Goal: The client will tell what could have been done to avoid problem situations, with 90% or greater accuracy.

Critical Thinking
Task R: Solving Complex Problems

1. Review the situation below and answer the questions.

   Russ and Pat went waterskiing early one morning before the lake got crowded. Pat was skiing and Russ was driving the boat. They were out in the middle of the lake when the motor suddenly stopped.

   a. Was that a problem? Why or why not? _____

   _____

   b. Why do you think the motor stopped? _____

   _____

   c. What could they do? _____

   _____

   Russ tried to restart the motor, but it wouldn't turn over. Pat swam toward the boat and Russ tried to pull her aboard, but she couldn't get over the side of the boat. The water was very cold and Pat began shivering.

   d. Why couldn't Pat get inside the boat? _____

   _____

   e. What would make it easier for Pat? _____

   _____

   There was no radio in the small boat.

   f. What should Pat and Russ do? _____

   _____

   g. What else could they do? _____

   _____

   h. What shouldn't they do? _____

   _____

I.E.P. Goal: The client will give appropriate answers to problem solving questions about everyday situations, with 90% or greater accuracy.

113   Copyright © 1988 LinguiSystems, Inc.

Task R: Solving Complex Problems, *continued*

2. Review the situation below and answer the questions.

Cindy, who is ten years old, was at the library after school. Her mother was supposed to pick her up on the corner near the library at 4:30. Cindy waited for her mom until 5:00, but her mother didn't show up.

a. Was that a problem? Why or why not? _____

_____

b. What should Cindy do? _____

_____

It began to get dark, so Cindy went back to the library to call her mom. The doors were locked.

c. What could Cindy do? _____

_____

Cindy went to the pay phone across the street. She dialed her home number, but no one answered.

d. Why didn't anyone answer the phone? _____

_____

Then, Cindy remembered that her mom had been out of town for the day and would pick her up on her way back into town. Cindy went back to the corner to wait.

e. Was that a good idea? Why or why not? _____

_____

Cindy's next door neighbor drove up and offered her a ride home. Cindy was about to accept the ride when she remembered she didn't have a house key.

f. What should Cindy do? _____

_____

g. What shouldn't she do? _____

_____

I.E.P. Goal: The client will give appropriate answers to problem solving questions about everyday situations, with 90% or greater accuracy.

3. Review the situation below and answer the questions.

Troy was taking a large bundle of clothes to the dry cleaners. He parked his car in the parking lot. He gathered the clothes from the car, locked the door, and pushed the door shut. As he shut the door, he saw his keys in the car.

a. What was the problem? _____

_____

b. Why do you think Troy locked the keys in the car? _____

_____

c. What should Troy do? _____

_____

Troy decided to take the clothes into the dry cleaners first. As he walked toward the door, he saw his car slowly rolling backwards, aimed at another car's bumper.

d. What did Troy forget to do? _____

e. What is the most important problem? _____

_____

f. What are some ways to solve this problem? _____

_____

_____

_____

g. What shouldn't Troy do? _____

_____

_____

4. Review the situation below and answer the questions.

Three boys went camping overnight in the mountains. Another friend dropped them off in the morning and arranged to pick them up the following morning. The boys hiked halfway up the mountain and decided to stop to swim in a lake. While they were swimming, some raccoons ate most of their food supplies and scattered the rest around the area.

a. What were the problems? _____

_____

_____

The boy who carried the matches forgot to take them out of his pocket before he went swimming.

b. What happened to the matches? _____

c. Was that a problem? Explain your answer. _____

_____

d. What should the boys do? List all the solutions you can think of.

_____

_____

_____

_____

e. What shouldn't the boys do? _____

_____

_____

_____

I.E.P. Goal: The client will give appropriate answers to problem solving questions about everyday situations, with 90% or greater accuracy.

5. Review the situation below and answer the questions.

Betsy has been getting crank phone calls at home at all hours of the day and night. The calls bother her and frighten her. She'd like to change to an unlisted number, but the phone company says it will take one month to make the change.

a. What are the problems? _____

_____

If Betsy gets her number changed to unlisted, she's worried her friends won't know how to reach her. Also, she has been interviewing for a new job and wants employers to be able to reach her by phone. Betsy could take the phone off the hook at night, but her mother is sick and might need to call her for help.

b. What is Betsy's most critical problem? _____

_____

c. What are some possible solutions to Betsy's problems? _____

_____

_____

_____

_____

d. What shouldn't Betsy do? Explain your answer. _____

_____

_____

I.E.P. Goal: The client will give appropriate answers to problem solving questions about everyday situations, with 90% or greater accuracy.

Task R: Solving Complex Problems, *continued*

6. Review the situation below and answer the questions.

Paul had to work late on Friday, so he couldn't cash his paycheck on the way home. He needed money for the weekend for groceries and to go out to dinner on Saturday.

a. What was the problem? _____

b. What could Paul do? _____

_____

Paul decided to use his bank card at an automatic teller machine and get some cash. He put his card in the machine and pressed the wrong keys for his identification number. The machine wouldn't give back his card. The message said he could recover his card from the bank in person on Monday.

c. What was the most important problem now? _____

_____

d. What could Paul do? _____

_____

_____

_____

e. What shouldn't Paul do? _____

_____

f. How could Paul have avoided this problem? _____

_____

I.E.P. Goal: The client will give appropriate answers to problem solving questions about everyday situations, with 90% or greater accuracy.

7. Review the situation below and answer the questions.

Matt was leaving his history class when a friend stopped him to talk about the prom. While they were talking, they placed their books and notebooks on the hall floor next to the wall. When they finished talking, they picked up their books to go home. When Matt got home, he realized he had picked up his friend's books instead of his own.

a. What were the problems? _____

_____

b. Why did Matt pick up his friend's books instead of his own? _____

_____

c. What is the most important problem? _____

_____

d. What should Matt do? Explain your answer. _____

_____

_____

_____

e. What shouldn't he do? _____

_____

_____

_____

8. Review the situation below and answer the questions.

Carol was horseback riding on some unfamiliar mountain trails. After riding for a couple of hours, she began to get hungry.

a. Was that a problem? Why or why not? _____

_____

b. What could Carol do? _____

_____

_____

_____

The sun was beginning to set and it was getting a bit chilly. Carol decided to ride home. As she rode along the trail, she came to a fork in the road. She didn't know which trail to take to go home.

c. What were the problems? _____

_____

_____

d. Which is the most important problem? Explain your answer. _____

_____

_____

e. What should Carol do? _____

_____

f. What shouldn't she do? _____

_____

I.E.P. Goal: The client will give appropriate answers to problem solving questions about everyday situations, with 90% or greater accuracy.

9. Review the situation below and answer the questions.

Val was invited to a surprise birthday party for Barb, her best friend. A week before the party, Barb called Val and invited her to a movie on Friday, the night of the party.

a. Was that a problem? Why or why not? _____

_____

b. What could Val do? _____

Caught offguard, Val agreed to go to the movie with Barb and they made plans to leave at 7:30 P.M., the same time the surprise party was to begin. Barb insisted on driving Val to the movie.

c. Why did Val agree to go to the movie with Barb? _____

_____

d. What is the most important problem? Why? _____

_____

e. What should Val do? List all the solutions you can think of. _____

_____

_____

_____

f. What shouldn't she do? _____

_____

I.E.P. Goal: The client will give appropriate answers to problem solving questions about everyday situations, with 90% or greater accuracy.

Task R: Solving Complex Problems, *continued*

10. Review the situation below and answer the questions.

    Larry was at home one winter evening. He decided to build a fire in the fireplace because it was getting chilly. He put in newspaper, kindling, and logs, and lit the fire. Suddenly, the room was full of smoke.

    a. What were the problems? _____

    _____

    b. Why do you think the room was full of smoke? _____

    _____

    c. What could Larry do? _____

    _____

    The smoke made Larry cough and it made his eyes sting.

    d. What was the most important problem? Explain your answer. _____

    _____

    _____

    e. What should Larry do? List all the possible solutions. _____

    _____

    _____

    _____

    f. What shouldn't he do? _____

    _____

    _____

    _____

I.E.P. Goal: The client will give appropriate answers to problem solving questions about everyday situations, with 90% or greater accuracy.

Task R: Solving Complex Problems, *continued*

11. Review the situation below and answer the questions.

Mike was very ill and missed three days of work. Since he had just started working

with the company, he was concerned that he had not yet accrued any sick leave.

a. What were the problems? _____

_____

_____

_____

Mike wondered if his employers thought him irresponsible since he missed three

days of work so soon after beginning the new job.

b. What is the most important problem? _____

_____

c. Why might Mike's employers consider him irresponsible? _____

_____

d. What should Mike do? _____

_____

_____

_____

e. What shouldn't he do? Explain your answer. _____

_____

_____

_____

I.E.P. Goal: The client will give appropriate answers to problem solving questions about everyday situations, with 90% or greater accuracy.

12. Review the situation below and answer the questions.

    April was preparing invitations for a birthday party for her son, Patrick. She had one more invitation to complete when she realized she had run out of the "clown" cards and matching envelopes.

    a. What was the problem? _____

    _____

    b. What could April do? List all the possible solutions. _____

    _____

    _____

    April went to the store to get another package of "clown" invitations, but they were all out.

    c. Was this a problem? Why or why not? _____

    _____

    April wanted the invitations to match the party decorations and reflect the "clown" theme. She asked the store to call other branches to see if the invitations were available, but no matching invitations could be found.

    d. Why did April want to buy another package of the "clown" invitations?

    _____

    e. Why did she ask the store to call other branches about the invitations?

    _____

    f. What is the most important problem? Why? _____

    _____

    g. What should April do? _____

    h. What shouldn't she do? _____

    _____

I.E.P. Goal: The client will give appropriate answers to problem solving questions about everyday situations, with 90% or greater accuracy.

13. Review the situation below and answer the questions.

Diane is completing her degree in accounting this semester. She has signed up for her classes, including two courses required for graduation. When she attends the first class of one of the required courses, she is told that the class is full and she has been dropped from the class.

a. Why was Diane dropped from the class? _____

_____

b. What were the problems? _____

_____

_____

c. What is the most important problem? Explain your answer. _____

_____

_____

d. What should Diane do? _____

_____

_____

e. What shouldn't she do? Why? _____

_____

_____

I.E.P. Goal: The client will give appropriate answers to problem solving questions about everyday situations, with 90% or greater accuracy.

14. Review the situation below and answer the questions.

Richard was flying to Boston for the weekend to be the best man in his brother's wedding. When he arrived at the airport, an announcement was made that no planes would fly to Boston due to a blizzard in that area. The Boston airport was closed until further notice.

a. Why were no planes flying to Boston? _____

_____

b. Was this a problem for Richard? Why or why not? _____

_____

c. What could Richard do? _____

_____

Richard needed to be in Boston by 10:00 A.M. the next day to attend the wedding at noon. He checked on the next available train and found out that it would arrive in Boston at 11:00 A.M., but that bad weather could delay it an hour or more.

d. Why is this a problem for Richard? _____

_____

e. What should Richard do? _____

_____

Some fellow passengers decided to rent a car and drive to Boston rather than take a plane or train. They invited Richard to join them.

f. What should Richard do? List all the possible solutions. _____

_____

_____

g. What shouldn't he do? _____

_____

I.E.P. Goal: The client will give appropriate answers to problem solving questions about everyday situations, with 90% or greater accuracy.

15. Review the situation below and answer the questions.

Deena decided to wallpaper her kitchen herself. She went to the store, bought the supplies, and hurried home to begin the job. As Deena began to hang the last roll of paper, she realized it didn't exactly match the other rolls already hanging on the walls.

a. Was this a problem? Why or why not? _____

_____

b. What could Deena do? _____

_____

It was late in the day and Deena knew the store was about to close. She was sure she had bought the last rolls of the pattern she wanted to use.

c. What were the problems? _____

_____

d. Which is the most important problem? _____

_____

e. What should Deena do? _____

_____

_____

_____

f. What shouldn't she do? _____

_____

_____

_____

I.E.P. Goal: The client will give appropriate answers to problem solving questions about everyday situations, with 90% or greater accuracy.

16. Review the situation below and answer the questions.

Andrew, a three year old, was playing downstairs in the den while his mother was cleaning the kitchen. He saw some small pieces of paper on the bathroom floor, picked them up, and put them in the toilet. He decided to help his mother by picking up other things and putting them in the toilet. Andrew proceeded to put things in the toilet until it was full.

a. What were the problems? _____

_____

b. How could the problems have been avoided? _____

_____

Andrew flushed the toilet. Water ran out onto the bathroom floor and the carpet in the den.

c. What was the problem? _____

_____

d. Why did water run onto the floor and the carpet? _____

_____

Andrew slipped in the water on the floor and began to cry.

e. Why did Andrew begin to cry? _____

_____

f. What was the most important problem? Why? _____

_____

g. What should Andrew's mother do? Give all the possible solutions. _____

_____

_____

h. What shouldn't she do? _____

_____

_____

I.E.P. Goal: The client will give appropriate answers to problem solving questions about everyday situations, with 90% or greater accuracy.

17. Review the situation below and answer the questions.

Rosemarie was doing her regular Thursday morning grocery shopping. When she arrived at the check-out, she remembered that she had no checks with her to pay for the groceries. She had forgotten to go by the bank on her way to the store that morning.

a. What was the problem? _____

_____

b. Why didn't Rosemarie have any checks with her? _____

_____

c. What could Rosemarie do? _____

_____

As the cashier finished ringing up her order, Rosemarie realized she only had five dollars in cash in her purse.

d. What were the problems? _____

_____

e. Which is the most important problem? Why? _____

_____

f. What should Rosemarie do? _____

_____

_____

g. What shouldn't she do? _____

_____

_____

I.E.P. Goal: The client will give appropriate answers to problem solving questions about everyday situations, with 90% or greater accuracy.

Task R: Solving Complex Problems, *continued*

18. Review the situation below and answer the questions.

Gary was enjoying a drive in the mountains when he stopped to admire the view. He was feeling hungry and tired, so he began the drive home. As he drove down the mountain, he applied the brakes often since the mountain was steep and there were many curves. Suddenly, the brakes failed.

a. What were the problems? _____

_____

b. Why did Gary apply the brakes often on his way down the mountain? _____

_____

c. Why did the brakes fail? _____

_____

d. What should Gary do? _____

_____

Gary couldn't get the brakes to work. He was having difficulty making the sharp turns on the curves near the bottom of the mountain.

e. What is the most important problem? Why? _____

_____

f. What should Gary do? Give all the possible solutions. _____

_____

_____

_____

g. What shouldn't he do? _____

_____

_____

_____

I.E.P. Goal: The client will give appropriate answers to problem solving questions about everyday situations, with 90% or greater accuracy.

19. Review the situation below and answer the questions.

Harold was driving his new car, a five-speed standard transmission, when it started to snow. As he drove up a steep hill, the car began to slide backwards.

a. What was the problem? _____

_____

b. Why did the car begin to slide backwards? _____

_____

c. What should Harold do? _____

_____

d. What shouldn't he do? _____

_____

Harold tried to step on the clutch to change gears, but he caught his pant leg on the seat lever. He couldn't move his leg.

e. Why couldn't Harold move his leg? _____

_____

f. What could Harold do? _____

_____

Harold's car began sliding into the other lane of traffic, near the edge of the road and a ravine.

g. What is the most important problem? _____

_____

h. What shouldn't Harold do? _____

_____

i. What are some ways to solve this problem? _____

_____

I.E.P. Goal: The client will give appropriate answers to problem solving questions about everyday situations, with 90% or greater accuracy.

20. Review the situation below and answer the questions.

    Gretchen decided to buy a new mattress and box springs for her attic bedroom. She went to the furniture store and selected a full-size mattress and box springs which were on sale. She scheduled delivery of the bedding for the next day. When it arrived, the movers couldn't get the box springs around the narrow turn into the attic stairwell.

    a. What was the problem? _____

    _____

    b. What could Gretchen do? _____

    _____

    c. What could the movers do? _____

    _____

    d. What shouldn't they do? _____

    _____

    Gretchen needed the bedding set up for overnight guests who were coming in that evening.

    e. What was the most important problem? _____

    _____

    Gretchen was unable to return the bedding to the store since purchases on all sale items were final.

    f. What should Gretchen do? Give all the possible solutions. _____

    _____

    _____

    g. What shouldn't she do? _____

    _____

    _____

I.E.P. Goal: The client will give appropriate answers to problem solving questions about everyday situations, with 90% or greater accuracy.

Critical Thinking: General Activities

1. Present students with a variety of objects that could be used to solve simple problems, such as tape, glue, money, a telephone directory, a needle and thread, etc. Describe problem situations and have the students choose objects which could be used to solve the problems. Have the students tell how the object functions. Be sure to include problems that could not be solved by using any of the objects in sight.

2. Give younger children activities which require them to improvise solutions. For example, remove certain crayons from the crayon box, a favorite chair from the reading circle, or key props from play areas to cause the children to improvise solutions for these environmental problems. Do this activity with individual children or with small groups.

3. Ask the student to share a problem he recently encountered. Identify the steps he used to solve the problem. Ask for alternative solutions which could have been used. Discuss the choice of solutions. Was the best solution chosen? Could a better solution have been reached under different circumstances?

    Help the student record these problems and solutions in a cumulative notebook. Look for patterns in his approach to problems (e.g., attack head on, wait and see, or seek help). Discuss these strategies for problem solving and notice the types of problems encountered most frequently.

4. Have your students play a game by choosing the correct category to solve a problem. Present an everyday problem. Then ask a student to choose which category of solution is required by selecting an object, information, or person card. For example, if the problem reads "It's time to move some heavy boxes to the attic," the student should choose a person card because physical help is needed. Have the student explain why he chose the person card.

    Once the students understand the game, choose teams to play. Each team receives one point for a correct response. The team with the most points at the end of the game wins.

5. Present problem situations and have the students role-play a solution. For example, one student could be a bank teller and another could be a customer without any identification who wants to withdraw cash. Discuss the role-playing with the students, and explain how this type of activity prepares them to deal with their own everyday problem situations.

6. Write various problem situations on cards. Shuffle the cards and deal several to each student. Have the students arrange their cards in relative order, least serious to most serious. Have them share their problem situations and explain why they arranged them in the order they chose. Note that these arrangements may vary due to personal experience or viewpoints.

7. Give a group of students a set of imaginary circumstances which require critical thinking. For example: "A five foot high electric fence surrounds your group. Each person must get over the fence without touching it. You can't go under the fence, you can't touch the fence, and you can't come back to help someone else once you've gotten out of the fence. You may reach over the fence, and students from the other side of the fence can help as long as they don't touch the fence." Encourage the students to work together to determine all possible solutions to the problem, and to select the best solution.

8. Read fairy tales, stories and nursery rhymes aloud. Discuss the problems that exist in the stories. Which problem is the most critical? Does a solution exist? What is the solution?

9. Have two students role-play a common problem situation. Have the other students watch for verbal expressions and body language that identify the problem. Videotape these activities to verify statements, body movements, changes in pitch, use of space, etc. Awareness of these areas will help your students communicate their problems, thoughts and feelings.

10. Present the students with a list of various occupations. Discuss each occupation, the types of problems workers might experience, ways of avoiding these problems, which problems would be the most critical to the workers, and possible solutions. For example, a working mother might have difficulty with child care, illness, and coordination of schedules.

Social Language

Social language skills involve using language as a tool to communicate with others. The child or adult with weak social language skills may communicate inadequately because he is unable to keep a conversation going or to explain his opinions easily. He may not be able to determine what information is pertinent and what is irrelevant.

The goal of social language training is to help the client develop functional language skills that will transfer to his everyday environment. The tasks in this section offer a broad base for developing social language skills. Tasks progress in complexity from focusing on critical information to general conversation skills.

Use your own judgment in presenting the tasks as oral or written exercises. Since conversation has few "right" or "wrong" responses, accept reasonable responses as correct. Answers are provided in the Answer Key only for tasks with fairly specific responses.

Provide conversation practice in a variety of realistic settings to help your client refine his social language skills in a natural context.

Task A: Requesting Information about Items

Ask questions to find out as much important information as you can about each item.
The first one is done for you.

1. car   <u>What model is the car?</u>   <u>What features does it have?</u>
      <u>Is it standard or automatic?</u>   <u>What make is it?</u>
      <u>What color is it?</u>   <u>How much does it cost?</u>

2. TV

3. house

4. book

5. dog

6. shirt

7. shoes

8. boat

I.E.P. Goal: The client will ask questions to find out pertinent information about items presented, with 90% or greater accuracy.

Task A: Requesting Information about Items, *continued*

Ask questions to find out as much important information as you can about each item.

9. photograph   _____   _____

                _____   _____

                _____   _____

10. flower   _____   _____

                _____   _____

                _____   _____

11. balloon   _____   _____

                _____   _____

                _____   _____

12. homework   _____   _____

                _____   _____

                _____   _____

13. magazine   _____   _____

                _____   _____

                _____   _____

14. game   _____   _____

                _____   _____

                _____   _____

15. mailbox   _____   _____

                _____   _____

                _____   _____

16. dessert   _____   _____

                _____   _____

                _____   _____

I.E.P. Goal: The client will ask questions to find out pertinent information about items presented, with 90% or greater accuracy.

Task A: **Requesting Information about Items**, *continued*

Ask questions to find out as much important information as you can about each item.

17. bus _____ _____

    _____ _____

    _____ _____

18. table _____ _____

    _____ _____

    _____ _____

19. sweater _____ _____

    _____ _____

    _____ _____

20. ticket _____ _____

    _____ _____

    _____ _____

21. bicycle _____ _____

    _____ _____

    _____ _____

22. pillow _____ _____

    _____ _____

    _____ _____

23. recipe _____ _____

    _____ _____

    _____ _____

24. new home _____ _____

    _____ _____

    _____ _____

I.E.P. Goal: The client will ask questions to find out pertinent information items presented, with 90% or greater accuracy.

Task A: Requesting Information about Items, *continued*

Ask questions to find out as much important information as you can about each item.

25. light bulb   _____   _____

    _____   _____

    _____   _____

26. movie   _____   _____

    _____   _____

    _____   _____

27. party   _____   _____

    _____   _____

    _____   _____

28. curtains   _____   _____

    _____   _____

    _____   _____

29. restaurant   _____   _____

    _____   _____

    _____   _____

30. stapler   _____   _____

    _____   _____

    _____   _____

31. glue   _____   _____

    _____   _____

    _____   _____

32. trail   _____   _____

    _____   _____

    _____   _____

I.E.P. Goal: The client will ask questions to find out pertinent information about items presented, with 90% or greater accuracy.

Ask questions to find out as much important information as you can about each item.

33. theater

_____   _____

_____   _____

_____   _____

34. mall

_____   _____

_____   _____

_____   _____

35. illness

_____   _____

_____   _____

_____   _____

36. vacation

_____   _____

_____   _____

_____   _____

37. calculator

_____   _____

_____   _____

_____   _____

38. biography

_____   _____

_____   _____

_____   _____

39. land

_____   _____

_____   _____

_____   _____

40. interview

_____   _____

_____   _____

_____   _____

I.E.P. Goal: The client will ask questions to find out pertinent information about items presented, with 90% or greater accuracy.

Task A: Requesting Information about Items, *continued*

Ask questions to find out as much important information as you can about each item.

41. microwave

42. election

43. outboard
     motor

44. computer

45. embassy

46. stained glass
     window

47. endangered
     species

48. appointment

I.E.P. Goal: The client will ask questions to find out pertinent information about items presented, with 90% or greater accuracy.

Task B: Requesting Information about Situations

Ask complete questions to find out the important information about the following situations. The first one is done for you.

1. A house is on fire.

    Are there people inside the house?

    Has the fire department been called?

    How did the fire start?

2. Your bedroom window is broken.

3. The door to your home is locked.

4. There is no picture on your TV set.

5. There is smoke coming from the basement.

6. Your pen won't write.

7. Your houseplant has wilted.

8. The syrup won't come out of the bottle.

I.E.P. Goal: *The client will ask questions to find out pertinent information about given situations, with 90% or greater accuracy.*

Task B: **Requesting Information about Situations**, *continued*

Ask complete questions to find out information about the following situations.

9. There is water in your basement.

_____

_____

_____

10. All the lights in your neighborhood are off.

_____

_____

_____

11. Traffic is backed up for three blocks ahead of you.

_____

_____

_____

12. Your ice cream in the freezer has melted.

_____

_____

_____

13. No water is coming out of your faucets.

_____

_____

_____

14. A light is flashing on your motel phone.

_____

_____

_____

15. Your car won't start.

_____

_____

_____

16. The copy machine is not working.

_____

_____

I.E.P. Goal: *The client will ask questions to find out pertinent information about given situations, with 90% or greater accuracy.*

Task B: Requesting Information about Situations, *continued*

Ask complete questions to find out important information about the following situations.

17. The dentist cancelled your appointment.

18. The automatic teller machine gobbled up your card.

19. A nurse from the hospital calls.

20. A neighbor is putting up a sign.

21. A house on the corner is boarded up.

22. There is music coming from your attic.

23. The governor is coming to your city.

24. You receive a letter from your mortgage company.

I.E.P. Goal: The client will ask questions to find out pertinent information about given situations, with 90% or greater accuracy.

Task C: Describing Common Events

Pretend you did each activity below and you want to tell someone about each event. Tell who was there, what you heard and saw, how it made you feel, who was with you, or any other information you would share in a conversation. The first one is done for you.

1. going to school on the first day

   I sat next to my best friend.   _I was glad to see John again._

   The new teacher is nice.   _The social studies class was boring._

   I ate lunch in the cafeteria.   _The kids were noisy in the halls._

2. going to the dentist's office

   _____   _____

   _____   _____

   _____   _____

3. marching in a parade

   _____   _____

   _____   _____

   _____   _____

4. being the guest of honor at a surprise party

   _____   _____

   _____   _____

   _____   _____

5. being in a storm at the beach

   _____   _____

   _____   _____

   _____   _____

6. riding the roller coaster

   _____   _____

   _____   _____

   _____   _____

I.E.P. Goal: The client will describe common events, with 90% or greater accuracy.

Task C: Describing Common Events, *continued*

Pretend you did each activity below and you want to tell someone about each event. Tell who was there, what you heard and saw, how it made you feel, who was with you, or any other information you would share in a conversation.

7. staying home from school after a thunderstorm

_____

_____

_____

8. bringing home an unsatisfactory report card

_____

_____

_____

9. moving into a new house

_____

_____

_____

10. going to a rock concert

_____

_____

_____

11. being afraid in the middle of the night

_____

_____

_____

12. getting a brand new bicycle

_____

_____

_____

I.E.P. Goal: The client will describe common events, with 90% or greater accuracy.

Task C: Describing Common Events, *continued*

Pretend you did each activity below and you want to tell someone about each event.
Tell who was there, what you heard and saw, how it made you feel, who was with you,
or any other information you would share in a conversation.

13. finding a bug in your salad

_____   _____

_____   _____

_____   _____

14. going trick-or-treating

_____   _____

_____   _____

_____   _____

15. going camping in a tent

_____   _____

_____   _____

_____   _____

16. getting up early to watch the sunrise

_____   _____

_____   _____

_____   _____

17. running out of gas in a strange town

_____   _____

_____   _____

_____   _____

18. winning an election

_____   _____

_____   _____

_____   _____

I.E.P. Goal: The client will describe common events, with 90% or greater accuracy.

Task C: Describing Common Events, *continued*

Pretend you did each activity below and you want to tell someone about each event. Tell who was there, what you heard and saw, how it made you feel, who was with you, or any other information you would share in a conversation.

19. taking your dog for a walk

_____   _____

_____   _____

_____   _____

20. spending the night with a friend

_____   _____

_____   _____

_____   _____

21. buying a present for someone

_____   _____

_____   _____

_____   _____

22. walking home after dark

_____   _____

_____   _____

_____   _____

23. swimming in the ocean

_____   _____

_____   _____

_____   _____

24. building a fire in the fireplace

_____   _____

_____   _____

_____   _____

I.E.P. Goal: The client will describe common events, with 90% or greater accuracy.

Task C: **Describing Common Events**, *continued*

Pretend you did each activity below and you want to tell someone about each event. Tell who was there, what you heard and saw, how it made you feel, who was with you, or any other information you would share in a conversation.

25. finding a lost pet

_____   _____

_____   _____

_____   _____

26. losing your wallet

_____   _____

_____   _____

_____   _____

27. arguing with a friend

_____   _____

_____   _____

_____   _____

28. receiving a package in the mail

_____   _____

_____   _____

_____   _____

29. having your picture taken by a photographer

_____   _____

_____   _____

_____   _____

30. making homemade ice cream

_____   _____

_____   _____

_____   _____

I.E.P. Goal: The client will describe common events, with 90% or greater accuracy.

Task D: Discriminating Appropriate Responses

Choose the polite response for each situation below. The first one is done for you.

1. If you like someone's dress, you say:

   (a.) "You look nice in that dress."
   b. nothing.

2. If you want more ice cream, you say:

   a. "I want more."
   b. "I'd like another bowl, please."

3. If someone calls for your sister and she isn't home, you say:

   a. "Please call back later."
   b. "She isn't home" and hang up.

4. If someone is talking loudly in the movie theater, you say:

   a. "Be quiet!"
   b. "Please talk quietly."

5. If your friend asks you if you like her new hairstyle, you say:

   a. "Oh, is it new?"
   b. "Yes, it looks very nice."

6. If you pull into a gas station and want to get gas at the full service pump, you say:

   a. "Fill the tank, please."
   b. "Give me gas" or "Fill it up."

7. If your friend's cigarette smoke keeps blowing in your face and it bothers you, you say:

   a. "Please don't smoke."
   b. "Yuk, get that cigarette away from me!"

8. If you think someone has done a good job on a hard project, you say:

   a. nothing. You just smile.
   b. "You really worked hard and it was worth it."

9. If you are trying to find cantaloupes in a new grocery store, you say:

   a. "Get me cantaloupe."
   b. "Where is the produce section?"

I.E.P. Goal: The client will choose the polite response to use in given situations, with 90% or greater accuracy.

Task D: Discriminating Appropriate Responses, *continued*

Choose the polite response for each situation below.

10. If you and a friend want to buy a submarine sandwich for lunch, you say:

    a. "Let's go to the deli."
    b. "Are you buying my lunch?"

11. If you think a clerk has given you incorrect change, you say:

    a. "You cheated me!"
    b. "I think you miscounted my change."

12. If you want to know how much it will cost to have your television fixed before you leave it to be repaired, you say:

    a. "I would like an estimate."
    b. "I won't pay for it if it costs too much."

13. If you are returning overdue library books, you say:

    a. "Why didn't you send me a reminder?"
    b. "I'm sorry these are late."

14. If you are trying to convince your best friend to try something new, you say:

    a. "Try it and see for yourself."
    b. "C'mon chicken, try it!"

15. If someone has hurt your feelings and you want to let them know, you say:

    a. "You hurt my feelings and now I'm mad."
    b. "I wish you had been more considerate of me."

16. If someone cooked you a great meal, you say:

    a. "It was good, but I didn't like the broccoli."
    b. "The meal was delicious!"

17. If your brother walks outside with his shoe untied, you say:

    a. "Don't trip, silly."
    b. "Your shoe is untied."

18. If your friend's dog is barking at you and you want it to stop, you say:

    a. "Let's go somewhere else so your dog won't be upset."
    b. "Make your dog leave me alone."

I.E.P. Goal: The client will choose the polite response to use in given situations, with 90% or greater accuracy.

Task D: Discriminating Appropriate Responses, *continued*

Choose the polite response for each situation below.

19. If you want to tell someone you like her, you say:

    a. "I like you — you're a special friend!"
    b. "You'll like me — I'm great!"

20. If your friend wins a prize in a contest, you say:

    a. "I know someone who won a better prize than you did."
    b. "Congratulations!"

21. If a man standing ahead of you in line at the grocery store has torn the back of his pants, you say:

    a. "Excuse me, your pants are ripped."
    b. nothing.

22. If someone calls for your father who is home ill, you say:

    a. "My father can't come to the phone right now. May I take a message?"
    b. "You can't talk to my father now. He's busy!"

23. If you have made reservations for dinner at a restaurant, you say:

    a. "Where's my table?"
    b. "I have reservations for dinner at 8:00."

24. If a salesperson wants to sell you something and you don't want to buy it, you say:

    a. "No, thank you. I'm not interested."
    b. "Leave me alone!"

25. If a friend gives you a present, you say:

    a. "I hope this is something I like."
    b. "Thank you for the present!"

26. If someone cuts your hair too short, you say:

    a. "My hair is a lot shorter than usual."
    b. "What did you do to my hair?"

27. If you break your mother's camera, you say:

    a. "I'm sorry I broke your camera."
    b. "It wasn't my fault! It's a cheap camera."

I.E.P. Goal: The client will choose the polite response to use in given situations, with 90% or greater accuracy.

Task E: Changing Meanings through Inflection

I'm going to say some sentences. Tell me what each sentence means in your own words. (Read each sentence, emphasizing the underlined words.) The first one is done for you.

1. I <u>won't</u> go on Thursday.
   I won't go on <u>Thursday</u>.
   <u>I</u> won't go on Thursday.

   I refuse to go.
   I'll go another day.
   Someone else may go.

2. We're having <u>pizza</u> for dinner?
   We're having pizza for <u>dinner</u>?
   <u>We're</u> having pizza for dinner.

3. I thought you'd be here at <u>nine</u>.
   I <u>thought</u> you'd be here at nine.
   I thought <u>you'd</u> be here at nine.

4. I can't believe you bought <u>me</u> a doll.
   I can't believe you bought me a <u>doll</u>.
   I can't believe <u>you</u> bought me a doll.

5. He walked <u>right</u> by me.
   He walked right by <u>me</u>.
   He <u>walked</u> right by me.

6. <u>Everyone</u> was at the gym.
   Everyone was at the <u>gym</u>.
   Everyone <u>was</u> at the gym.

7. <u>Some</u> of the cookies were burned.
   Some of the <u>cookies</u> were burned.
   Some of the cookies were <u>burned</u>.

8. John <u>thinks</u> he's going to win the election.
   <u>John</u> thinks he's going to win the election.
   John thinks he's going to <u>win</u> the election.

9. <u>No</u> radios should be allowed in the library.
   No radios should be allowed <u>in</u> the library.
   No radios <u>should</u> be allowed in the library.

10. <u>Do</u> you believe what you just said?
    Do you <u>believe</u> what you just said?
    Do <u>you</u> believe what you just said?

11. No one ever helps <u>me</u>.
    <u>No</u> one ever helps me.
    <u>No</u> one ever <u>helps</u> me.

12. Her <u>last</u> name is Sharon.
    Her <u>last</u> name <u>is</u> Sharon.
    <u>Her</u> last name <u>is</u> Sharon.

I.E.P. Goal: The client will interpret the meanings of inflectional changes in identical sentences, with 90% or greater accuracy.

Task F: Determining Whether Statements Start, Maintain, or Finish a Conversation

Tell whether each comment starts, maintains, or finishes a conversation. Some comments may have more than one use in conversations. The first one is done for you.

1. "Hi."	<u>starts</u>	maintains	finishes
2. "Good evening."	starts	maintains	finishes
3. "Are we ready to begin?"	starts	maintains	finishes
4. "Fine, thanks. How are you?"	starts	maintains	finishes
5. "It's all gone."	starts	maintains	finishes
6. "What's your name?"	starts	maintains	finishes
7. "He really did that?"	starts	maintains	finishes
8. "Do you mean today?"	starts	maintains	finishes
9. "Did I leave it in the car?"	starts	maintains	finishes
10. "Hurry back!"	starts	maintains	finishes
11. "Jane, may I speak with you?"	starts	maintains	finishes
12. "See you tomorrow!"	starts	maintains	finishes
13. "Maybe."	starts	maintains	finishes
14. "Happy birthday!"	starts	maintains	finishes
15. "I agree."	starts	maintains	finishes
16. "Once upon a time, . . ."	starts	maintains	finishes
17. "Thank you for your help."	starts	maintains	finishes
18. "I'll call back later. "	starts	maintains	finishes
19. "Ladies and gentlemen, . . ."	starts	maintains	finishes
20. "In conclusion, . . ."	starts	maintains	finishes
21. "Yes, I know, but . . ."	starts	maintains	finishes
22. "May I help you?"	starts	maintains	finishes
23. "My name is Jean."	starts	maintains	finishes
24. "I'm done."	starts	maintains	finishes

I.E.P. Goal: The client will determine whether comments start, maintain, or finish a conversation, with 90% or greater accuracy.

Task G: Initiating Conversations

Tell what you would say to start a conversation in the following situations. The first one is done for you.

1. A new student has just entered school.

   What school did you go to before you came here?

2. You meet two neighbors while walking around the block.

   _____

3. You see a little boy who is lost in a department store.

   _____

4. You need help at the gas station.

   _____

5. Your grandmother has come for a visit.

   _____

6. You are ready to order at a restaurant.

   _____

7. The mail carrier is delivering your mail.

   _____

8. You meet your teacher on the first day of school.

   _____

9. You want something from behind the counter at the bakery.

   _____

10. You bring a birthday present to a friend.

    _____

11. Friends from out of town come to your house.

    _____

12. The repair person has come to fix your television.

    _____

I.E.P. Goal: When presented with various situations, the client will give appropriate sentences to begin conversations, with 90% or greater accuracy.

Task G: **Initiating Conversations**, *continued*

Tell what you would say to start a conversation in the following situations.

13. Your sister has come home for vacation.

_____

14. You are checking in at a hotel.

_____

15. A stranger is riding in an elevator with you.

_____

16. You need help from a telephone operator.

_____

17. A motorist has just hit your car.

_____

18. You see a stranger who is a guest at a party you are attending.

_____

19. A police officer has just pulled you over.

_____

20. You're waiting in line to see a movie.

_____

21. A stranger is standing in your front yard.

_____

22. A friend just had a baby.

_____

23. You broke a friend's plate while you were washing dishes.

_____

24. You take your sick child to the doctor.

_____

I.E.P. Goal: When presented with various situations, the client will give appropriate sentences to begin conversations, with 90% or greater accuracy.

Task H: Taking One Topic Turn

Each item below starts a conversation. Tell a question or a sentence that would keep the conversation going. The first one is done for you.

Note: If this task is done orally, complete each topic turn by responding to the client's statement.

1. I just read an article written by a man who claims to have been inside a UFO.

   <u>What did he say it was like inside the UFO?</u>

2. My favorite ride at an amusement park is the Ferris wheel.

   _____

3. Cats are smarter than dogs.

   _____

4. I think children should go to school twelve months a year instead of nine.

   _____

5. If I could have any dessert I wanted, I'd choose chocolate cheese cake.

   _____

6. I think trains are a lot safer for travel than airplanes.

   _____

7. *The Cat in the Hat* is the best children's book ever written.

   _____

8. The beach is the only place to go for a great vacation.

   _____

9. The Fourth of July is the most exciting holiday because of the fireworks.

   _____

10. The best rock 'n' roll group of all times is the "Beatles."

    _____

11. What would we do without friends to depend on?

    _____

12. Fall is the best season of the year.

    _____

I.E.P. Goal: When presented with questions or statements that begin a conversation, the client will provide a statement maintaining each topic, with 90% or greater accuracy.

Task H: Taking One Topic Turn, *continued*

Each item below starts a conversation. Tell a question or a sentence that would keep the conversation going.

Note: If this task is done orally, complete each topic turn by responding to the client's statement.

13. The jobs I dislike doing the most are washing the dishes and taking out the garbage.

_____

14. One of the greatest events in a young teenager's life is getting her first job.

_____

15. My grandpa believes in sleeping with the windows open no matter how cold it is.

_____

16. I remember when the ice cream truck used to drive around our neighborhood in the summer.

_____

17. I couldn't function at work without the help of my secretary. She does everything!

_____

18. It must be fun to have a twin brother or sister.

_____

19. I remember when you could buy a loaf of bread for twenty cents.

_____

20. I'm not sure that a vegetable garden saves you very much money after you pay for all the seeds and fertilizer.

_____

21. Yesterday, I had one of the most frightening experiences of my life.

_____

22. I wonder what life will be like one hundred years from now.

_____

23. When I went to the grocery store, I saw a mouse in the dog food section.

_____

I.E.P. Goal: When presented with questions or statements that begin a conversation, the client will provide a statement maintaining each topic, with 90% or greater accuracy.

Task H: Taking One Topic Turn, *continued*

Each item below starts a conversation. Tell a question or a sentence that would keep the conversation going.

Note: If this task is done orally, complete each topic turn by responding to the client's statement.

24. The best Halloween I ever had was when we made our own haunted house.

   _____

25. At my cousin's wedding last summer, the groom never showed up.

   _____

26. When I went to the dentist, she told me I had the best teeth she had seen in weeks.

   _____

27. There is so much you can learn in a public library.

   _____

28. The caboose is an important part of a train.

   _____

29. A basketball game is enjoyed by young and old alike.

   _____

30. Concerts can be indoors or outdoors, classical or modern.

   _____

31. It is so peaceful sitting on a river bank, fishing the afternoon away.

   _____

32. Housekeeping is one of the most boring, routine tasks on earth.

   _____

33. I learned so much in my photography class.

   _____

34. There is nothing better than reading a good book while lying in a hammock on a warm spring day.

   _____

I.E.P. Goal: When presented with questions or statements that begin a conversation, the client will provide a statement maintaining each topic, with 90% or greater accuracy.

Task I: Requesting Action, Assistance or Information

Pretend that you are in the following situations. Answer each question by making an appropriate comment. The first one is done for you.

1. Your little sister is chasing her ball, which has rolled into the street. What do you say to her?

    Stop! There's a car coming!

2. You are taking your dog for a walk and he jumps up on your neighbor. What do you say to your dog?

3. Your brother is eating a candy bar. You are very hungry and he has another one in his pocket. What do you say to him?

4. Your teacher is getting ready to dismiss your class for the day. She took your softball because you were playing with it in class. You want to play with it tonight. What do you say to her?

5. Your brother's car is parked behind yours in the driveway. You need to use your car to go to work. What do you say to your brother?

6. You have left a roll of film at the drugstore to be developed. What do you say to the clerk when you go back to the store?

7. Your doctor's appointment is at 4 P.M. At twenty minutes past four, your name has not been called. You need to be home by 6:00 P.M. What do you say to the receptionist?

8. You have come to a dance by yourself. You see someone else who is alone and you would like to meet him. What do you say to him?

I.E.P. Goal: When presented with situations, the client will make appropriate statements requesting action, assistance or information, with 90% or greater accuracy.

Task I: Requesting Action, Assistance or Information, *continued*

Pretend that you are in the following situations. Answer each question by making an appropriate comment.

9. You are in charge of the neighborhood parade. You need ten volunteers to help you line up the marchers. You have a list of fifteen volunteers. What do you say when you call them?

   _____

10. Last week, you made a reservation to stay at a motel. When you arrive, the desk clerk does not have a reservation for you. What do you say to the clerk?

   _____

11. You are sitting in the front seat of the car while your mother backs out of the driveway. All of a sudden, a car comes speeding around the corner. What do you say to your mother?

   _____

12. You have been standing in line at the bakery for ten minutes. Just when it is your turn, a lady walks in and steps in front of you. What do you say to her?

   _____

13. While you are cooking dinner, a salesperson calls you on the telephone wanting to sell you something. What do you say to the salesperson?

   _____

14. You are a fourth grade teacher. The children are having recess in the classroom. You are ready to begin the afternoon math lesson. What do you say to the students?

   _____

15. You are dining at a restaurant. You are finished eating and you want to pay the bill. What do you say to the waiter?

   _____

16. You are attending a concert. You really enjoy the performance and you want to see more after it is finished. What do you say?

   _____

I.E.P. Goal: When presented with situations, the client will make appropriate statements requesting action, assistance or information, with 90% or greater accuracy.

Pretend that you are in the following situations. Answer each question by making an appropriate comment.

17. You are riding home with your friend and you begin to feel sick from the motion of the car. What do you say to your friend?

_____

18. You are walking toward your car in the parking lot. You see someone trying to open one of the doors. What do you say to him?

_____

19. You are a train conductor and the train is getting ready to leave the station. What do you say to the passengers standing outside the train?

_____

20. While climbing a mountain with friends, you knock loose some rocks with your foot. What do you say to the climbers below you?

_____

21. You are watching a movie at the theater. A woman sitting in front of you begins talking in a loud voice. What do you say?

_____

22. You are a state trooper and you have pulled someone over for speeding. What do you say to him?

_____

23. While riding your bicycle you approach a jogger from behind who is running more slowly than you are riding. What do you say to her?

_____

24. You are a dentist. You have just given a patient a shot of Novocain so that he will not feel the drill as you fix a tooth. You want to make sure the Novocain has taken effect. What do you say to the patient?

_____

I.E.P. Goal: When presented with situations, the client will make appropriate statements requesting action, assistance or information, with 90% or greater accuracy.

Task J: Terminating Conversations

For each situation below, provide the last sentence or two to terminate the conversation. The first one is done for you.

1. You have invited a friend to a party. She says, "I'm free on Saturday." What would you say?

   I'm glad you can come. See you at 8:00.

2. The clerk in the store doesn't have what you want. She says, "I'm sorry, we don't have that in stock." What would you say?

   _____

3. You have just beaten your friend at tennis. He says, "You played a great game!" What would you say?

   _____

4. Your friend says, "May I borrow your snow shovel?" What would you say?

   _____

5. A co-worker asks, "Could you give me a lift home?" What would you say?

   _____

6. Your friend has won a scholarship to college. She says, "I'm so excited about the scholarship!" What would you say?

   _____

7. Your friend has returned your bicycle with a flat tire. He says, "Sorry about the tire!" What would you say?

   _____

8. Your father is leaving on a business trip. He says, "I'll see you on Friday." What would you say?

   _____

9. The newspaper boy has not delivered your paper for several days. He says, "I keep forgetting to leave one at your house." What would you say?

   _____

I.E.P. Goal: The client will provide the final sentences to terminate conversations appropriately, with 90% or greater accuracy.

Task J: Terminating Conversations, *continued*

For each situation below, provide the last sentence or two to terminate the conversation.

10. A friend has just given you a gift. She says, "I hope you like it." What would you say?

_____

11. A person on your softball team has missed the last two games. He says, "I had a sprained ankle." What would you say?

_____

12. You are leaving a friend's house after dinner. She says, "Thanks for coming!" What would you say?

_____

13. Your banker says, "I'm sorry. You don't qualify for a loan right now." What would you say?

_____

14. Your uncle says, "You forgot my birthday last week." What would you say?

_____

15. Your boss has given you a promotion and a raise. He says, "You're a good employee." What would you say?

_____

16. Your mother says, "Oh, no, you broke my favorite vase!" What would you say?

_____

17. Your best friend says, "My father was in a car accident yesterday." What would you say?

_____

18. A friend says, "Would you like to go to dinner on Tuesday?" What would you say?

_____

I.E.P. Goal: The client will provide the final sentences to terminate conversations appropriately, with 90% or greater accuracy.

For each situation below, provide the last sentence or two to terminate the conversation.

19. You ask your parents if you can spend the night with a friend. Your mother says, "Not tonight." What would you say?

_____

20. A child who lives next door has broken your bedroom window. His mother says, "It was an accident." What would you say?

_____

21. Your dentist says, "You have three cavities." What would you say?

_____

22. You buy some popcorn at the movies. The clerk says, "Would you like anything else?" What would you say?

_____

23. Your mother calls to tell you she missed seeing you over the weekend. She says, "I wish you would visit more often." What would you say?

_____

24. You have accidently backed your car into another car in the parking lot. The driver of the other car gets out and says, "It doesn't look as though much damage has been done." What would you say?

_____

25. A repairman comes to your home to fix the washing machine. He was supposed to fix it yesterday. He says, "I'm sorry, I didn't come yesterday." What would you say?

_____

26. Your cousin is leaving your home after visiting for a week. She says, "See you next year!" What would you say?

_____

27. You are babysitting a child and have told him twice to go to bed. He says, "My mother lets me stay up and watch TV." What would you say?

_____

I.E.P. Goal: The client will provide the final sentences to terminate conversations appropriately, with 90% or greater accuracy.

Task K: Making Inferences from Observations

Read the statements below. Tell all the ways you would know each statement below is true. The first one is done for you.

1. It's Saturday morning.

   Cartoons are on television.
   The newspaper has "Saturday" on it.
   School is closed.

2. It's going to rain.

3. A store is open.

4. You need a haircut.

5. A plant needs water.

6. The oven is on.

7. The mail carrier has come to your house.

8. The refrigerator is broken.

I.E.P. Goal: When presented with possible conclusions, the client will give possible observations supporting those conclusions, with 90% or greater accuracy.

Task K: Making Inferences from Observations, *continued*

Tell all the ways you would know each statement below is true.

9. You need a new pair of
   shoes.

   _____

   _____

   _____

10. Your soup is cool
    enough to eat.

    _____

    _____

    _____

11. Spring is on the way.

    _____

    _____

    _____

12. It's a holiday.

    _____

    _____

    _____

13. The popcorn is ready
    to eat.

    _____

    _____

    _____

14. Your dog needs to go
    outside.

    _____

    _____

    _____

15. The cake is done.

    _____

    _____

    _____

16. The school bus has already
    been to your stop.

    _____

    _____

I.E.P. Goal: When presented with possible conclusions, the client will give possible observations supporting those conclusions, with 90% or greater accuracy.

Task K: Making Inferences from Observations, *continued*

Tell all the ways you would know each statement below is true.

17. Your pencil needs to be sharpened.

_____

_____

_____

18. Your bicycle tires need air.

_____

_____

_____

19. A bill is overdue.

_____

_____

_____

20. A pond is shallow.

_____

_____

_____

21. Your car needs a tune-up.

_____

_____

_____

22. You have driven 500 miles on a trip.

_____

_____

_____

23. Your furnace isn't working.

_____

_____

_____

24. The clock is keeping correct time.

_____

_____

_____

I.E.P. Goal: When presented with possible conclusions, the client will give possible observations supporting those conclusions, with 90% or greater accuracy.

Task L: Telling Why Situations Could Not Occur

Tell why you couldn't do each item below. The first one is done for you.

1. Why couldn't you eat cereal with a fork?

   The milk would stay in the bowl.

2. Why couldn't you write with a broken pencil?

   _____

3. Why couldn't you dig a hole in the ground with a snow shovel?

   _____

4. Why couldn't you hang wallpaper with tape?

   _____

5. Why couldn't you cross a desert in a boat?

   _____

6. Why couldn't you fly a kite in the house?

   _____

7. Why couldn't you drive a car without tires?

   _____

8. Why couldn't you mail a letter without a stamp?

   _____

9. Why couldn't you fry an egg without breaking it?

   _____

10. Why couldn't you do jumping jacks in a telephone booth?

    _____

11. Why couldn't you play basketball while wearing snow skis?

    _____

12. Why couldn't you watch television if the power went off?

    _____

I.E.P. Goal: The client will tell why situations could not occur, with 90% or greater accuracy.

Task L: Telling Why Situations Could Not Occur, *continued*

Tell why you couldn't do each item below.

13. Why couldn't you train your dog to do your homework?

_____

14. Why couldn't you wear your gloves on your feet?

_____

15. Why couldn't you store Popsicles in the stove?

_____

16. Why couldn't you bake a cake in the sun?

_____

17. Why couldn't you get on an airplane while carrying a gun?

_____

18. Why couldn't you adopt a twin brother?

_____

19. Why couldn't you sleep standing up?

_____

20. Why couldn't you climb a tree with a broken arm?

_____

21. Why couldn't you eat popcorn without cooking it?

_____

22. Why couldn't you divide an orange in half without cutting the skin?

_____

23. Why couldn't you find a friend's number in the telephone book if you didn't know his last name?

_____

24. Why couldn't you divide 75¢ evenly between yourself and a friend?

_____

I.E.P. Goal: The client will tell why situations could not occur, with 90% or greater accuracy.

Task M: Telling Why Situations Should Not Occur

Tell why you shouldn't do each item below. The first one is done for you.

1. Why shouldn't you leave your crayons in the sun?

   <u>They will melt.</u>

2. Why shouldn't you leave the milk out of the refrigerator?

   _____

3. Why shouldn't you eat a big lunch before running a race?

   _____

4. Why shouldn't you dive into the shallow end of a swimming pool?

   _____

5. Why shouldn't you share a cup with someone who has a cold?

   _____

6. Why shouldn't you leave roller skates on the stairs?

   _____

7. Why shouldn't you leave your jacket in the park?

   _____

8. Why shouldn't you leave your car unlocked while you are shopping in the mall?

   _____

9. Why shouldn't you water your houseplants every day?

   _____

10. Why shouldn't you get in the bathtub before testing the water?

    _____

11. Why shouldn't you wear a big hat on a windy day?

    _____

12. Why shouldn't you shake a soft drink before opening it?

    _____

I.E.P. Goal: The client will tell why situations should not occur, with 90% or greater accuracy.

Task M: Telling Why Situations Should Not Occur, *continued*

Tell why you shouldn't do each item below.

13. Why shouldn't you wash your favorite shirt with the dog's blanket?

_____

14. Why shouldn't you drive at night while wearing sunglasses?

_____

15. Why shouldn't you leave your bike in the yard at night?

_____

16. Why shouldn't you leave a wet towel on a wooden table?

_____

17. Why shouldn't you pour grease down the kitchen sink?

_____

18. Why shouldn't you ride your bike down the middle of the street?

_____

19. Why shouldn't you look directly at the sun?

_____

20. Why shouldn't you use gasoline to start a fire in the fireplace?

_____

21. Why shouldn't you change a light bulb while the lamp is turned on?

_____

22. Why shouldn't you ride in a boat without your life jacket?

_____

23. Why shouldn't you fly a kite in a thunderstorm?

_____

24. Why shouldn't you give a stranger your name and address?

_____

25. Why shouldn't you let a baby play in the yard alone?

_____

I.E.P. Goal: The client will tell why situations should not occur, with 90% or greater accuracy.

Task N: Denying Statements

Use a complete sentence to deny each statement and give the correct information. The first one is done for you.

1. Your name is Smith.

   No, my name is not Smith, it's Wilson.

2. You live in Russia.

   _____

3. Christmas comes in March.

   _____

4. You cook toast in the refrigerator.

   _____

5. A child drives a car.

   _____

6. John is a girl's name.

   _____

7. You use a broom to rake leaves.

   _____

8. People wear shorts when it's cold outside.

   _____

9. You heat a tea bag in the oven to make tea.

   _____

10. You wash laundry in the furnace.

    _____

11. A long-distance operator helps you send a letter.

    _____

12. You wear mittens on your ears to keep warm.

    _____

I.E.P. Goal: When presented with false statements, the client will deny the accuracy of the statements and provide the correct information, using complete sentences, with 90% or greater accuracy.

Task N: **Denying Statements**, *continued*

Use a complete sentence to deny each statement and give the correct information.

13. You sleep during the day.

_____

14. People eat nails for lunch.

_____

15. You wear a boot on your head.

_____

16. A bathtub is used for swimming.

_____

17. You eat bugs for snacks.

_____

18. Dogs live in trees.

_____

19. You use buttons to purchase things.

_____

20. Glasses help people to hear better.

_____

21. A flagpole is used to sleep on.

_____

22. You wear clothes to take a bath.

_____

23. A doctor takes your order in a restaurant.

_____

24. Children live at the zoo.

_____

I.E.P. Goal: When presented with false statements, the client will deny the accuracy of the statements and provide the correct information, using complete sentences, with 90% or greater accuracy.

Task O: Denying That Given Statements Are True

Use a sentence to show why each statement isn't true. The first one is done for you.

1. All birds can fly.

   <u>Penguins can't fly.</u>

2. School principals must be at least six feet tall.

   _____

3. Doctors must have a driver's license to practice medicine.

   _____

4. Good friends never keep secrets from each other.

   _____

5. Drinking orange juice every day keeps you from getting the flu.

   _____

6. If you want to be an actor, you must first learn how to sing and dance.

   _____

7. All holidays fall on a Saturday.

   _____

8. All hurricanes are named after girls.

   _____

9. Cars are the only source of pollution in our cities.

   _____

10. Only government officials are allowed to own and display U.S. flags.

    _____

11. All rivers in the U.S. empty into the Atlantic Ocean.

    _____

12. The largest city in each state serves as the state capital.

    _____

I.E.P. Goal: When presented with false statements, the client will deny the statements by presenting counter examples, with 90% or greater accuracy.

Task O: Denying That Given Statements Are True, *continued*

Use a sentence to show why each statement isn't true.

13. Only men can become U.S. Supreme Court justices.

_____

14. All people living in the U.S. are American citizens.

_____

15. All airplane crashes since 1984 have been due to pilot error.

_____

16. All music written after 1962 is classified as rock 'n' roll.

_____

17. The Winter Olympics must be held every four years in Europe.

_____

18. All cars manufactured in the U.S. must have four doors.

_____

19. Telephone books must list everyone's first and last names.

_____

20. Television stations are only allowed to broadcast violent programs after 9:00 P.M.

_____

21. All students entering a university must be at least seventeen years old.

_____

22. All cities with a population of more than 200,000 have mass transit systems.

_____

23. George Washington was the only U.S. president who was a farmer.

_____

24. All presidential candidates in the U.S. run on the Democratic or Republican ticket.

_____

I.E.P. Goal: When presented with false statements, the client will deny the statements by presenting counter examples, with 90% or greater accuracy.

Task P: Requesting Information about Opinions

Ask someone to give you his opinion about one or more of the issues below. Then, state your own opinion about the issue, agreeing or disagreeing with the other person. The first one is done for you.

1. stores being open on Sunday

   Should stores be open on Sunday? Yes, you might need to shop.

2. keeping wild animals in zoos

   _____

3. smoking in restaurants

   _____

4. advertising for Christmas before Halloween

   _____

5. letting girls play Little League football

   _____

6. violence on television

   _____

7. having children with handicaps in classrooms with nonhandicapped students

   _____

8. letting children attend funerals

   _____

9. the cost of prescription drugs

   _____

10. allowing alcohol advertising on television

    _____

11. teachers' salaries

    _____

12. movie rating systems

    _____

I.E.P. Goal: The client will ask another person for his opinion on issues and respond with his own opinion, with 90% or greater accuracy.

Task P: Requesting Information about Opinions, *continued*

Ask someone to give you his opinion about one or more of the issues below. Then, state your own opinion about the issue, agreeing or disagreeing with the other person.

13. professional athletes' salaries

_____

14. raising the speed limit on interstate highways

_____

15. teaching children to read before they start kindergarten

_____

16. buying foreign-made products

_____

17. allowing fourteen year olds to drive a car

_____

18. state lotteries

_____

19. single men or women adopting children

_____

20. limiting the president to one term of office

_____

21. daylight savings time

_____

22. the safety records of major airlines

_____

23. creating a national holiday in August

_____

24. signing an organ donor card

_____

I.E.P. Goal: The client will ask another person for his opinion on issues and respond with his own opinion, with 90% or greater accuracy.

Task Q: Changing Conversational Topics

You'll need a partner for this task. One person will begin a conversation with a sentence or two about the first topic. At the right time, the other person will shift the conversation to the second topic. Topic changes should be natural and not abrupt. The first one is done for you.

1. cats → dogs

   first speaker: "I think cats are wonderful pets. They are clean and affectionate."

   second speaker: "I like cats, but dogs are my favorite pet."

2. football → baseball

   first speaker: "Going to a football game is great fun. Even if it rains or snows, you can still have a good time."

3. hula hoops → Frisbees

   first speaker: "You have to practice in order to spin a hula hoop. It's easier to practice outside because you have more room."

4. horseback riding → hiking

   first speaker: "We went horseback riding in the mountains. It was a wonderful way to get to the top."

5. movies → plays

   first speaker: "I think going to a movie is great entertainment! Some actors really make their characters seem real."

6. traveling by train → traveling by car

   first speaker: "I really miss traveling by train. We used to take a trip on a train at least once a year."

7. building a snowman → sleigh riding

   first speaker: "Building a snowman is a nice winter activity. It's fun being outside."

8. water skiing → snow skiing

   first speaker: "Have you ever been water skiing? I skied on vacation last summer."

I.E.P. Goal: Given a set of topics, the client will make an appropriate shift from one topic to another in a natural manner, with 90% or greater accuracy.

Task Q: Changing Conversational Topics, *continued*

You'll need a partner for this task. One person will begin a conversation with a sentence or two about the first topic. At the right time, the other person will shift the conversation to the second topic. Topic changes should be natural and not abrupt.

9. being the youngest child → being the oldest child

   first speaker: "I'm the youngest child in our family. Sometimes it's hard because your older brothers and sisters can do things that you can't."

10. radio → TV

   first speaker: "Some people listen to music on the radio, but I like to listen to the news."

11. Ferris wheel → merry-go-round

   first speaker: "I love to go to the carnival so I can ride the Ferris wheel. It's really fun when it stops and you're on the top."

12. rodeo → hockey

   first speaker: "Have you ever been to a western rodeo? It's exciting when the riders are on your side of the arena."

13. the high price of groceries → growing your own food

   first speaker: "I can't believe how much I spend when I go to the grocery store! Food prices just keep going up!"

14. woodworking → pottery

   first speaker: "I just finished making a cradle for my sister's baby. I really enjoy working with wood."

15. piano lessons → rock bands

   first speaker: "I'm trying to convince my daughter to take piano lessons. She doesn't realize that the piano is basic to most music."

16. congressmen → elections

   first speaker: "We have a very good congressman from our district. He truly cares about the people he represents."

17. space travel → the Pilgrims

   first speaker: "I think you have to like the unknown to travel into space. It takes a great deal of courage."

I.E.P. Goal: Given a set of topics, the client will make an appropriate shift from one topic to another in a natural manner, with 90% or greater accuracy.

Social Language: General Activities

1. Provide younger students with a variety of masks, costumes, puppets, paper dolls, etc., to practice role-playing. If necessary, provide a lead into each activity such as a short introduction in story form. The same format also can be used to practice topic turns. After a topic is established, each character should stay on the topic for an appropriate number of responses.

2. Present the student with situations which require your help. For example, ask her to give you the time if there is no clock, but you're wearing a watch, or lock the door to a cabinet and ask her to get something from it. Encourage the student to use complete sentences to request your help, and to tell you why she needs your help.

3. Present a topic to the group. Have one client provide the beginning statement. Have the remaining group members take one topic turn on the subject. The last person in the group will provide the terminating sentence to complete the topic discussion. Alternate roles so that all members of the group can practice beginning, maintaining and ending a conversation.

4. Have two students role-play an emotional, verbal argument. Ask another student to enter the conversation. Provide two or three different approaches this student might use (e.g., she might try to distract them by trying to change the topic or she might enter into the argument in order to find out why it started and how it might be resolved.) Discussion after the role-play should focus on the appropriateness of the student's remarks, her actions, and the content of her questions and statements. What kind of information was she able to obtain during the argument?

5. Ask a student to write a one page paper on a topic you've chosen. Provide an encyclopedia and reference books on the topic. Help the student find the information he will need in the reference books. Review how to initiate the topic of the paper in the beginning paragraph, how to maintain the topic throughout the paragraph and how to terminate the paragraph. This activity should illustrate to the student how verbal, pragmatic skills can be adapted to written activities.

6. To practice shifting the topic in conversation, write various conversation topics on slips of paper. Give each student several slips. Begin a conversation focused on one topic and tell the students that during the next ten minutes, each student should successfully shift the conversation to each of the topics on his slip. Vary the amount of time, depending on size of the group, skill levels of students and complexity of the topics. Begin with topics that are related (e.g., summer vacation, the Fourth of July, and going to the beach) and progress to topics that are tangentially related or unrelated (e.g., the price of automobiles, public transportation, the Presidential election, and women's roles in society).

7. Present the group with a list of fifteen to twenty nouns, verbs, adjectives and adverbs. Give them ten minutes to write a short paragraph. Ask them to use the listed words to tell a story. Have them analyze their paragraph. How many of the words did they use? How appropriate was the sentence structure? Did things happen in logical order?

   For younger children, use a more restrictive vocabulary of five to ten words and present the story in outline form, asking them to fill in the blanks where appropriate.

8. Create a mock banquet with guests seated around a long table. Give each guest a role to play, such as a doctor, housewife, engineer, author, or car salesman. Place construction paper labels around the table representing food items, such as roast beef, vegetable casserole, butter, rolls, salt, pepper, and milk. Ask the guests to fill their plates with food by using a complete sentence to ask the person closest to the food item to pass it. Once served, each guest should initiate at least three topics of conversation and shift topics twice. Conversations about topics should incorporate at least two to four turns. Adjust topic turn requirements to suit students' abilities.

9. Have students pretend to be newspaper or television reporters. Have them practice beginning, maintaining and ending conversations and requesting information. Give students a specific list of information they must obtain or they may make up their own as they speak. Use a variety of interesting situations (e.g., an interview with the person who invents a means of turning garbage into gold; an interview with the first female President of the United States; an interview with residents of the long lost continent, Atlantis) or historical situations (e.g., interviewing General Washington at Valley Forge, interviewing Indians about the first settlers, interviewing Susan B. Anthony about women's suffrage) to make the exercise fun. Role-play an uncooperative person being interviewed to give the students the opportunity to use pragmatic conversational skills in difficult situations.

10. With a group of four or five, assign each one a different role to play while completing a group task such as: deciding on a lunch menu, making up a song about whales, recommending a new traffic pattern for the neighborhood. The roles you assign could include: the mediator, the joker, the complainer, the procrastinator, the taskmaster, the agitator, the know-it-all, and the doubter. Each client's role is a secret. At the end of the time period, have group members discuss how each one helped or prevented completion of the task. Let group members try to guess each other's roles.

ANSWER KEY

Concepts

Task A   pages 8-9

1. bathroom
2. kitchen
3. purse
4. closet
5. toy box
6. bureau, dresser
7. lunchbox
8. closet
9. refrigerator
10. house
11. laundry room
12. utensil drawer
13. toolbox
14. desk
15. park, playground
16. sewing box
17. pantry or cupboard
18. linen closet
19. car trunk
20. nursery
21. doghouse
22. medicine cabinet
23. gym locker
24. spice rack
25. wallet
26. pocket
27. diaper bag
28. briefcase, desk
29. doctor's office
30. church
31. beachbag
32. backpack or knapsack
33. library
34. office
35. shopping center
36. airport
37. book
38. porch
39. garage, toolshed
40. gym
41. file cabinet
42. safe-deposit box

Task B   pages 10-11

1. on
2. in
3. beside
4. in
5. in front of
6. over
7. in
8. through
9. at
10. after
11. in
12. outside
13. into
14. up
15. in
16. beside
17. in
18. on
19. over
20. on the front
21. through
22. under
23. at
24. at
25. down
26. up
27. to

28. away from
29. through
30. on
31. over
32. out of
33. in
34. on
35. across
36. close to
37. over
38. through
39. away from
40. among

Task C   pages 12-13

1. under; on
2. through; off
3. up; down
4. between; over, on, off
5. around; down
6. in; on
7. inside; outside
8. in; on
9. under; on
10. on; in
11. behind; in front of
12. below; over, above
13. in; on
14. under; over
15. below; in front of
16. bottom; top
17. outside; inside
18. below; above, over
19. behind; in front of
20. above; below, under
21. over; under
22. in, on
23. in front of; in back of, behind
24. away from; next to, beside
25. between; in

Task D   pages 14-15

1. *on* the stereo, *in* its jacket
2. *around* your waist
3. *in* your hair
4. *in* the ocean, *across* the water
5. *on* your wrist
6. *in* a socket
7. *at* the end of a train
8. *under* the ground
9. *behind* bars, *in* prison
10. *on* a roof, *on* the ground
11. *between* the goal posts
12. *over* your friend
13. *at* a post office
14. *in* a pool, *in* a lake
15. *through* a mountain
16. *on* your hands
17. *in* a wallet, *in* a bank
18. *between* the bread slices
19. *around* the neck
20. *on* a pillow
21. *on* the toothbrush
22. *at* the bull's-eye
23. *in front of* the mirror
24. *between* your teeth, *in* the bathroom
25. *in* the ignition
26. *over* the plate, *to* the hitter

27. *between* two cars, *in* a parking lot
28. *around* your neck
29. *toward* the flag
30. *through* the eye of the needle
31. *over* a fireplace, *above* a fireplace
32. *around* the present
33. *across* water
34. *against* the shore, *on* the beach
35. *through* the meat
36. *toward* the finish line, *on* a track
37. *in* the White House, *in* Washington, D.C.
38. *at* a bank, *from* a bank
39. *outside* a city
40. *against* a wall

Task E   pages 16-17

1. ice cream float
2. peanut butter and jelly sandwich
3. chocolate milk
4. cole slaw
5. tossed salad
6. lemonade
7. cinnamon toast
8. tuna fish sandwich
9. milk shake
10. pizza
11. fruit salad
12. bacon-lettuce-tomato sandwich
13. peanut butter
14. salad dressing
15. onion dip
16. cheeseburger
17. hoagie, submarine sandwich
18. bread
19. potato salad
20. s'mores
21. fries, potato chips
22. apple pie
23. cake
24. beef stew
25. chicken soup
26. jelly
27. chili
28. cocktail sauce
29. sloppy joes
30. succotash

Task F   pages 18-19

1. buy a pair of pants
2. clean a house
3. give a dog a bath
4. have a birthday party
5. make a long distance phone call
6. mail a letter
7. hang a picture
8. take pictures
9. do laundry
10. fry chicken
11. play football
12. go to the grocery store
13. watch a parade
14. make a garment
15. build a fire
16. go to the beach

17. go water skiing
18. make a banana split
19. put on make up
20. get glasses
21. buy a car
22. plant a garden
23. write a paper
24. get married
25. take a vacation
26. make a deposit
27. apply for a job
28. prepare income taxes
29. buy real estate
30. run for an office

Task G   pages 20-21

1. brown, rough
2. stretchy, wooly
3. cute
4. sharp, sturdy
5. light, long, pointed
6. cold, hard
7. fragile, portable
8. gooey
9. bright, luminous, hot
10. handy, sharp
11. bumpy, nutritious
12. helpful, obedient
13. jointed
14. useful, decorative, expensive
15. solid, firm
16. festive
17. oval
18. large, furry
19. circular
20. handy, functional
21. uncivilized
22. rapid, noisy, streamlined
23. comfortable, soft
24. learned, impartial
25. fluffy, airy
26. trained, caring
27. liquid, flammable
28. helpful, sequential
29. festive, fun
30. organized, lengthy
31. feline, fierce
32. extra, rewarding
33. challenging, irregular
34. lengthy, intriguing
35. silent, mute
36. sandy

Task H   pages 22-25

1. round; can be rolled, kicked, thrown, bounced, etc.; available in many colors
2. has four wheels; driven; has an engine; runs on gasoline
3. is outdoors; has sides; filled with sand; children play in it
4. has on/off switch; has a shade; powered by electricity, gas or oil; helps us see at night
5. children play with it; some talk or cry; some are made of paper

183

Copyright © 1988 LinguiSystems, Inc.

6. opens and closes; on hinges; has handle or doorknob; keeps out wind and noise
7. an animal; has four legs; barks; likes bones
8. built of brick or wood; has doors and windows; family lives in it
9. is alive; gives shade; birds live in it; leaves fall off in autumn
10. has pages; has a cover; written by an author; in a library
11. piece of furniture; different sizes; covered with sheets and blankets; sleep in it
12. rings; has receiver; can be dialed; talk on it
13. made of canvas; has straps; can be worn on back; carry things in it
14. form of transportation; runs on tracks; has many cars; runs on diesel fuel
15. sharp; it removes hair; metal blade; can be electric
16. lets water leave a sink; is metal; gets clogged; it's hard to see down it
17. gives light; has wick; made from wax; can be scented
18. cools us off; can be electric; can hang from ceiling; has blades
19. protects table; dishes are set on it; can be made of cloth; restaurants have paper ones
20. loyal; likes us; helps us with problems; fun to be with
21. fun; marching bands; floats; loud
22. fun; don't go to work; lasts a week or two; people go on trips during one
23. big; has a deep and shallow end; filled with water; has a drain
24. majestic; high; snow-capped; can be climbed
25. sold in drugstores; stops perspiration; smells good; goes under arms
26. long; made of asphalt; two or four lanes; cars travel on it
27. many trees in it; fruit is grown there; bees like it
28. ceremony; happy time; has bride and groom; guests eat cake
29. ceremony; sad time; friends and relatives attend; expensive
30. place to keep money; get one at bank; is numbered; protected

31. follows pattern; planned; lists days and times; helps keep track
32. dangerous; skilled physicians perform it; get anesthesia before it; can help us get well
33. has memory; instructs us; stores files; uses programs
34. in courtroom; has judge and jury; legal procedure; decides guilt or innocence
35. every four years; amateurs compete; happen in summer and winter; inspiring
36. candidate is chosen; people vote; ballots are cast; should be fair
37. has animals; exciting; dangerous; has clowns
38. has pews; quiet; has an altar; people worship in it
39. formal; students wear caps and gowns; students get diplomas; students leave school
40. on TV; has cast of characters; has many commercials
41. protects our head; hard; used for sports; has a chin strap
42. made of paper; has advertisements; comes in the mail; contains articles
43. contains many items; has colorful pictures; comes in the mail; we buy things from it
44. information is presented; group of people; may follow rules
45. long; has characters; has a plot; entertaining
46. includes land and buildings; listed in the newspaper; purchased
47. a preventative step; written as a policy; pays for medical expenses; sold by different companies
48. moisture; rain; snow; falls from the sky

Task I page 26

1. yes
2. no
3. no
4. yes
5. no
6. yes
7. yes
8. yes
9. no
10. yes
11. no
12. yes
13. yes
14. no
15. yes
16. no
17. yes
18. yes
19. yes

20. no
21. yes
22. yes
23. no
24. yes
25. no

Task J pages 27-28

Answers will vary depending upon individual preference and reasoning.

Task K pages 29-30

1. before
2. last
3. during
4. last
5. during
6. after
7. in the middle
8. at the end
9. morning
10. right now
11. after
12. before
13. after
14. after
15. before
16. follow
17. during
18. tomorrow
19. afternoon
20. follow
21. before
22. first
23. night
24. following
25. already
26. precede
27. long time ago
28. in a short time
29. at the same time
30. simultaneously

Task L pages 31-33

1. movie
2. roller coaster
3. funeral
4. hockey
5. car
6. vacation
7. beautician
8. game of racquetball
9. chess
10. across town
11. air conditioner
12. debate
13. tennis
14. on a motorcycle
15. museum
16. on a picnic
17. being elected to an office
18. christening
19. hot bath
20. free concert
21. running track
22. backgammon
23. gymnast
24. yogurt
25. expired driver's license
26. driving a car
27. pneumonia
28. to swim

29. a symphony
30. climbing a mountain
31. witnessing an accident
32. felony
33. presidential inauguration
34. breaking one's leg
35. flat tire
36. jumping hurdles

Task M page 34

(Note: Reverse order is equally acceptable.)

1. cold, warm, hot
2. small, big, huge
3. dusty, dirty, filthy
4. upset, angry, livid
5. dry, damp, wet
6. calm, lively, frantic
7. cool, cold, frigid
8. large, great, stupendous
9. lucky, unfortunate, tragic
10. silent, quiet, loud
11. moderate, costly, exorbitant
12. incorrect, accurate, precise
13. unknown, familiar, intimate
14. frightful, shocking, hideous
15. popular, unliked, infamous
16. cowardly, timid, bold
17. tired, fatigued, exhausted
18. amusing, funny, hilarious
19. unhappy, distressed, inconsolable
20. deficient, adequate, perfect
21. frugal, generous, extravagant
22. satisfactory, noteworthy, outstanding
23. negligent, careful, painstaking
24. embarrassed, humiliated, mortified
25. unimportant, pressing, urgent

Task N pages 35-36

1. stone age
2. train
3. Columbus' voyage
4. Civil War
5. Native Americans
6. pyramids
7. discovery of electricity
8. video cassette recorder
9. General Eisenhower
10. World War II
11. Mark Twain
12. the Wright brothers' flight
13. United States Constitution
14. George Washington
15. printing press
16. sailboat
17. inauguration of President Reagan
18. Alaska
19. Rome

20. limb amputations
21. John Kennedy
22. sinking of the *Titanic*
23. the World Series
24. smallpox

Task O   page 37

1. yes
2. no
3. yes
4. yes
5. no
6. no
7. yes
8. no
9. yes
10. no
11. yes
12. yes
13. yes
14. no
15. yes
16. no
17. yes
18. yes
19. no
20. yes
21. no
22. yes
23. yes
24. no
25. no

Paraphrasing

Task A   pages 42-43

1. sick, ill
2. automobile, car
3. cool, chilly
4. antique, old
5. garbage, trash
6. rich, wealthy
7. fat, overweight
8. tired, fatigued
9. happy, glad
10. big, large
11. beautiful, attractive
12. afraid, frightened
13. funny, amusing
14. intelligent, smart
15. delightful, charming
16. handy, convenient
17. moist, damp
18. hard, difficult
19. gentle, mild
20. lift, raise
21. thick, dense
22. donate, give
23. fresh, new
24. late, tardy
25. firm, stiff
26. broken, fragmented
27. honest, truthful
28. obedient, compliant
29. accurate, correct
30. fair, objective
31. physician, doctor
32. mature, ripe
33. difficult, complex
34. college, university
35. pale, ashen
36. opponent, enemy
37. prompt, punctual

38. interpret, explain
39. patience, endurance
40. anticipate, expect
41. reimburse, pay
42. fictional, imaginary
43. profit, gain
44. isolated, alone
45. maternal, motherly
46. perfect, infallible
47. humble, modest
48. convalesce, recuperate
49. trio, triad
50. somber, serious

Task B   pages 44-45

1. up, down
2. black, white
3. noisy, quiet
4. old, new
5. right, left
6. dry, wet
7. light, heavy
8. day, night
9. kind, cruel
10. go, come
11. empty, full
12. short, tall
13. big, little
14. rude, polite
15. child, adult
16. friend, enemy
17. dull, sharp
18. female, male
19. forward, backward
20. part, whole
21. safe, dangerous
22. quick, slow
23. repair, break
24. steady, jerky
25. considerate, thoughtless
26. wrong, correct
27. same, different
28. positive, negative
29. admit, deny
30. strict, lenient
31. interior, exterior
32. genuine, fake
33. sturdy, fragile
34. absurd, sensible
35. unusual, common
36. defeat, victory
37. praise, criticize
38. painful, pleasant
39. vertical, horizontal
40. serious, humorous
41. hidden, obvious
42. elated, dismayed
43. conceal, identify
44. object, agree
45. coordinated, clumsy
46. greedy, generous
47. capable, incompetent
48. conservative, liberal
49. boring, interesting
50. clear, ambiguous

Task C   pages 46-47

1. slow
2. straight
3. sweet
4. hard
5. smooth
6. small
7. fancy

8. thin
9. hard
10. loud
11. serious
12. sorry
13. full
14. clear
15. doughy
16. exciting
17. young
18. warm
19. curved
20. stuck-up
21. messy
22. dry
23. cool
24. large
25. stuffy
26. smooth
27. tidy
28. full
29. gentle
30. weak
31. confident
32. elated
33. courteous
34. dull
35. cheap
36. sturdy
37. free
38. short
39. flexible
40. appealing
41. mature
42. inaccurate
43. rough
44. angry
45. bland
46. ill
47. miniature
48. energetic
49. plain
50. husky

Task D   pages 48-49

1. sheriff
2. bagel
3. tissue
4. quilt
5. jacket
6. clippers
7. rug
8. crayon
9. restaurant
10. wrench
11. pipe
12. auditorium
13. cradle
14. hard hat
15. cup
16. horse
17. baby
18. spot remover
19. calendar
20. tweezers
21. watch
22. surfboard
23. blinds
24. job
25. latch
26. photograph
27. ladle
28. ledge
29. pasture
30. Band-Aid

31. trench
32. adding machine
33. pickle
34. magazine
35. tune
36. coyote
37. bus
38. prescription
39. trail
40. designer

Task E   pages 50-51

1. bat, mitt; baseball things
2. crown, hat; things worn on the head
3. satin, linen; fabrics
4. corn, oats; grains
5. sapphire, ruby; jewels
6. bracelet, necklace, watch; jewelry
7. puck, racquet; sports equipment
8. ax, drill, pliers; tools
9. banjo, trumpet; musical instruments
10. hornet, bee; insects
11. broccoli, shamrocks, peas; green things
12. reading, physics, mathematics; school subjects
13. Thanksgiving, Easter, New Year's; holidays
14. oval, triangle; shapes
15. tracks, caboose, locomotive; things that go with a train
16. stapler, paper clip; paper fasteners
17. Earth, Jupiter; planets
18. Monopoly, kickball, checkers; board games
19. ding, boom, pop; noises, sounds
20. macadamia, hickory; types of nuts
21. fork, knife; eating utensils
22. bucket, canteen; water containers
23. chef, artist, secretary; occupations
24. run, crawl, slide; verbs, actions
25. rubber band, muscles, bubble gum; things that stretch
26. Idaho, Vermont, Illinois; states
27. Mexico, Peru; countries
28. hepatitis, chicken pox; contagious diseases
29. brass, bronze, silver; metals
30. Andy, Ted, Carl; boys' names
31. waltz, tango; types of dances
32. fish, crab, octopus; ocean animals
33. parrot, dove; birds
34. pen, pencil; writing utensils
35. fire, sun; hot things
36. cider, soda; beverages

37. calf, chicken, sheep; farm animals
38. table, couch, chair; furniture
39. airplane, bicycle; vehicles
40. book, magazine, sign; things to read
41. poppy, daffodil, tulip; flowers
42. robin, airplane, butterfly; things that fly
43. ball, marble, pearl; round things
44. heart, brain, liver; organs
45. grapefruit, kiwi, lime; fruits
46. glue, mayonnaise, jelly; things you spread
47. noun, verb, adjective; parts of speech
48. burglary, larceny; crimes
49. Democratic, Independent, Republican; political parties
50. sympathy, fear, remorse; emotions

Task F page 52

1. yes
2. no
3. yes
4. no
5. yes
6. no
7. no
8. yes
9. no
10. yes
11. no
12. yes
13. no
14. no
15. yes
16. yes
17. no
18. yes
19. no
20. yes
21. no
22. yes
23. no
24. no
25. yes

Task G pages 53-54

1. yes
2. no
3. yes
4. no
5. no
6. yes
7. yes
8. no
9. yes
10. no
11. yes
12. no
13. yes
14. no
15. yes
16. yes
17. no
18. no
19. yes

20. no
21. yes
22. no
23. yes
24. yes
25. yes
26. no
27. yes
28. no
29. yes
30. no
31. no
32. yes
33. no
34. yes
35. no
36. yes
37. no
38. no
39. yes
40. no
41. yes
42. no
43. no
44. yes
45. no
46. yes
47. yes
48. no
49. yes
50. yes

Task H pages 55-57

1. Jerome is ill.
2. Randa is attractive.
3. Wendy was chilly sitting outside.
4. Chad wanted to talk to the police officer.
5. Tom was happy to see his mom.
6. Jan was too mad to listen.
7. Len was frightened by ghosts.
8. Ben tore the paper.
9. An elephant is huge.
10. Fred got the job done in a hurry.
11. The wading pool is not very deep.
12. This steak is chewy.
13. The bread had just been made.
14. Lou's statement was not true.
15. Mary is very giving.
16. The ceremony is about to start.
17. The food in that restaurant costs a lot of money.
18. The baby's bib was moist.
19. The chest of drawers was old.
20. The trail was very hazardous.
21. The restroom was sterile.
22. The presentation was finished.
23. The slaves wanted to be free.
24. This novel is not a true story.

25. That picture is unattractive.
26. The store manager is working hard.
27. Maddie is wealthy.
28. Carl went on vacation.
29. Frank said the job wouldn't last long.
30. The pond water was not muddy.
31. The new bus schedules are not the same.
32. Katie is selfish.
33. The secretary's typing was flawless.
34. Brian's comment was very humiliating.
35. This material can catch on fire.
36. The disease is very contagious.

Task I pages 58-60

1. The lake looks calm.
2. Bob is in a bad mood today.
3. Just look at that sunset.
4. I definitely don't need another job.
5. When I lost the election, Dad told me to be tough.
6. I am very nervous.
7. Sandra was very happy.
8. Norman doesn't say very much.
9. Ted treats me like a child.
10. My teacher really makes us work hard.
11. This math is simple to do.
12. Our new television was very expensive.
13. If Ed doesn't take that job, he will be hurting himself.
14. When my brakes failed, I thought I would die.
15. My grandma always says to do what you want and let other people do what they want.
16. Now that her children are gone, she can do anything she wants to do.
17. Jean is involved in too many things.
18. I love Karen as if she were a member of my own family.
19. George acts like a very old man.
20. That's everything that happened at the fair.
21. Mr. Henderson seems like a nice person, but he really isn't.
22. My uncle looked very uncomfortable at the wedding reception.
23. Lisa looks very suspicious.
24. We got this china very inexpensively at a yard sale.

25. Suzanne certainly is graceful.
26. Taking care of the baby is hard work.
27. I just don't know where I put my address book.
28. Their marriage isn't a very happy one.
29. Lee is always there when he's needed.
30. The main character in this novel is nuts.
31. Our neighbors moved away and left their house completely empty.
32. If you tell him what I said, it will only make things worse.
33. I'll never let you drive my new car!
34. I heard the Stevens' new business is in trouble.
35. The children were drawn to the storyteller.
36. It was really hard for me to get tickets for the playoff game.

Task J pages 61-62

1. I really liked the movie.
2. I'll never eat there again.
3. I don't like children.
4. I really admire Ms. Correlli.
5. I don't like the Richardsons.
6. I thought the history exam was very easy.
7. I'm irritated that my sister wants me to wash her clothes.
8. I think my pediatrician is wonderful.
9. I'm worried about something more important than what to wear to the party.
10. I'd really like to go to England.
11. I really need some help.
12. Mr. Nelson avoided me.
13. Joel always acts like he is mad.
14. I don't think you should wear that dress to the wedding.
15. I'm very tired or I'm very hungry.
16. You can buy that stereo very cheaply.
17. I like Lynn, but I don't think she is very bright.
18. I just can't do anything about it.
19. I don't think Jose is a good artist.
20. I don't think your priorities are in the right order.
21. I've loaned many books to friends who never return them.
22. If I don't get a raise, we'll have to stop spending so much money.

23. Allen isn't a very good public speaker.
24. Let's decide which things are the most important to get done today.

Task K pages 63-64

1. We should stay away from the back of our yard.
2. Karen was well on Friday.
3. There will only be four guests at the party.
4. If it doesn't rain, the event will be held outdoors.
5. We may wear soft-soled shoes on the boat.
6. Ben hasn't arrived yet.
7. You never went to the shore during other seasons.
8. You don't like mustard.
9. They must be home.
10. The film must be stored in a dark place.
11. Then I left because I didn't think you were coming.
12. She made higher marks than any other student.
13. No one was thinking about anything else.
14. Lily does not disagree with her parents.
15. Maude is not interested in competition with other schools.
16. Mr. LePeter and his business partners are not honest.
17. The colors of the portrait were very light.
18. Mr. Damien spoke another language better.
19. It was easy to see the trees and rocks, but not the house.
20. The professor was hard to understand.
21. The tree clipping crew did not sit around.
22. Dominic and Rosa agreed on most things.
23. Kurt is an unusual doctor.
24. The takeover wasn't a last-minute decision.

Task L pages 65-68

Answers will vary.

Critical Thinking

Task A pages 72-73

1. egg, frying pan, spatula, fork
2. envelope, address, stamp, pen
3. kite, string, wind
4. cake mix, cake pan, water, eggs, spoon
5. bathtub, water, soap, towel, washcloth
6. mop, water, bucket, cleanser
7. telephone, telephone number
8. water, sink, detergent, dish cloth
9. paint, paper, smock
10. towel, bathing suit, suntan lotion, pool/lake
11. books, assignment, paper, pencil/pen
12. wood, matches, kindling
13. chair for each player, record player, records
14. bus schedule, bus stop, fare
15. make-up, baggy pants, funny hair, hat
16. iron, ironing board, spray starch
17. fishing pole, line, hook, bait
18. washing machine, detergent, water
19. taco shells, lettuce, meat, tomatoes, cheese
20. shovel, water, potting soil
21. phone number, telephone, operator
22. car, keys, license, insurance
23. shaving cream, razor, after-shave lotion
24. baseball, bat, mitt
25. window cleaner, rags, ladder
26. lawn mower, gas, oil
27. knitting needles, yarn, pattern
28. flour, eggs, sugar, spoon, cookie sheet, oven
29. cars, floats, bands, spectators
30. television, electricity, program schedule
31. ground beef, tomatoes, seasonings, spaghetti noodles
32. oil, wrench, oil pan, rags
33. dough, tomato sauce, toppings, pizza pan
34. wood, tar paper, shingles, nails, hammer
35. money, lawyer, bank loan
36. money, florist, friend's name and address
37. dog's description, newspaper, friends
38. bingo cards, markers, callers, numbers
39. ground coffee, coffeepot, water
40. newspaper ads, application, skills, interview

Task B pages 74-75

1. cake, invitations, ice cream
2. thread, needle
3. hose, plants, shovel
4. nails, glue
5. glass, putty
6. ax, saw
7. stamps, address, envelope
8. nail, hammer
9. antiseptic, bandage
10. ribbon, tape, scissors
11. jack, crowbar
12. tar paper, shingles, nails
13. physician
14. optometrist
15. veterinarian
16. diplomat
17. thesaurus, dictionary
18. exterminator
19. topic, title
20. audiometer
21. attorney, lawyer
22. filter, strainer
23. piano tuner
24. calculator, adding machine

Task C pages 76-77

1. Decide what kind to order.
2. Find out what's playing.
3. Take off your clothes.
4. Dig holes.
5. Get the lawn mower.
6. Go to the shoe store.
7. Write the letter.
8. Make a snowball.
9. Choose teams.
10. Decide when it will be.
11. Sort the dirty clothes.
12. Gather logs.
13. Get the ingredients out.
14. Put down a drop cloth.
15. Get out the hose, bucket, soap and rags.
16. Look for it.
17. Turn off the light switch.
18. Decide where to go.
19. Boil water.
20. Take off the dirty diaper.
21. Hard boil the eggs.
22. Make an appointment.
23. Find the recipe.
24. Get the vacuum cleaner.
25. Look in the newspaper.
26. Decide on a topic.
27. Decide on the date.
28. Take the tire off.
29. Find the receipt.
30. Find out where the leak is.
31. Read the directions.
32. Shut off the water supply.
33. Get out your bank statement and checkbook.
34. Find out the size of tire needed.
35. Look up the call number.
36. Sand the floor.
37. Find jumper cables.
38. Compliment him.
39. Fill out a loan application.
40. Set the alarm.

Task D pages 78-80

1. the phone number
2. what kind, how many boxes
3. what size, how many
4. need sun or shade, when to plant, how deep to plant
5. your name, which clothes, which store
6. magazine name, where to deliver it, how many issues
7. how many pizzas, what toppings
8. what size, what style, how much to spend
9. who it's for, what's the occasion
10. where, what day, what time
11. who it's for, what he likes, what size he wears
12. your address, where the person is coming from, names of streets in between, where to turn
13. how much to take, how often, how many days, any restrictions
14. what happened, where, who was involved
15. what size, what color, what style
16. what day you can go, what time you can go, what the problem is
17. how many people, what time
18. the height and width of the pane
19. which rental stores are open, which type of tape, which movie
20. his name, his size, his breed, where he was last seen
21. what water temperature to use, whether it fades, if it can be put in the dryer
22. what and when to feed it, where parent will be
23. name, address, age, social security number, how much you need to borrow, what the money is for, names of references
24. name, past experience, education, hours available, when the person can begin
25. what size pattern, what types of fabrics, how much fabric, what notions needed
26. how much it is, where to mail the bill
27. what weight it takes, where it goes
28. which one has burned out, what size
29. address, birthday date
30. boy or girl, size
31. number of miles for each way, type of road conditions

ANSWER KEY

32. best seed for your climate and amount of sun
33. party affiliations, past performance, campaign pledges
34. traffic laws, hours bureau is open
35. amounts of checks, withdrawals and deposits; current balance
36. furnished or unfurnished; deposit; utilities payment

Task E pages 81-83

1. Put the plant in the hole.
2. Pour some milk into the glass.
3. Put toothpaste on your toothbrush.
4. Pour juice into the holders.
5. Deposit coins.
6. Break the lettuce into a bowl.
7. Set the power and time controls.
8. Go to the restaurant.
9. Tape the paper.
10. Add detergent.
11. Put the pillows on the bed.
12. Put the car in reverse.
13. Deal out the money and set up the bank.
14. Thread a needle.
15. Put on a clean diaper.
16. Turn the pancakes over with a spatula.
17. Write a check for each bill.
18. Put the hose in the pool.

Task F pages 84-85

1. The paper will catch on fire.
2. The eggs will break.
3. It will float away
4. It will be hard boiled.
5. The ice cream will melt.
6. It will be returned to you.
7. It will overflow.
8. The coins will fall out.
9. You will burn your hands.
10. The tire will go flat.
11. You will fail in school.
12. The tissue will fall apart.
13. You may be fired.
14. The bulb will burn out.
15. It will ruin the cake.
16. An accident will happen.
17. Ice will form
18. The flowers will wilt and die.
19. You cannot enter the country.
20. The picture will be black.
21. You will run into another car; you will get a ticket.
22. The wall will fall down when it gets wet.
23. You will win the election.
24. You will make a song.

Task G pages 86-87

1. tricycle—It's easier to balance.
2. buying a sweater—You don't have to know how to knit.
3. jumping over a stick—It's smaller.
4. answering the phone—You don't have to remember numbers.
5. folding a towel—It's smaller.
6. cutting a twig—It's smaller and easier to cut.
7. doing a chore—It is done faster.
8. getting a haircut—All you need to do is sit still.
9. driving a car—It's easier to maneuver.
10. lighting a lamp—You just flip a switch.
11. playing catch—It requires little skill.
12. making ice—You just put water in the freezer.
13. making instant coffee—You don't have to assemble the coffee pot.
14. putting on glasses—They don't require cleaning and inserting.
15. painting a wall—You don't have to work over your head.
16. adding two numbers—You don't have to know multiplication tables.
17. skiing cross-country—You travel on more level ground.
18. making toast—You don't need a recipe.
19. operating a motorboat—You don't need to maneuver sails.
20. dancing a waltz—It has fewer, simpler steps.
21. adding whole numbers—You don't need to find the common denominator.
22. reading a magazine—It's shorter.
23. playing a harmonica—You don't need to read music.
24. watching a video tape—You just sit and watch.

Task H pages 88-89

1. yes—Her cake burned.
2. no
3. yes—The ice cream fell off.
4. no
5. yes—The balloon had a hole in it.
6. no
7. yes—He had no money to pay for dinner.
8. no
9. yes—It popped.
10. yes—The roof was leaking.
11. no
12. yes—The iron might start a fire.
13. no
14. yes—They knocked over the trash.
15. yes—The light bulb blew out.
16. no
17. no
18. yes—He is ill.
19. yes—The car was running out of gas.
20. no
21. yes—They might fall through the ice.
22. yes—She is locked out in her bathrobe.
23. no
24. no

Task I pages 90-91

1. He needs a leash.
2. She has no toothbrush.
3. He couldn't take off his jacket.
4. The freezer is broken or turned to low.
5. She can't finish the test.
6. You have no matches.
7. The milk was sour.
8. The picture tube is broken.
9. Your pants ripped.
10. She missed the bus.
11. He ran out of paper.
12. He stepped on some gum.
13. He broke a neighbor's window.
14. The shoes are too small.
15. He used the wrong key.
16. She had no hot water.
17. It boiled over.
18. The line was busy.
19. The circuts are overloaded.
20. The drain is stopped up.
21. You have cavities.
22. She won't be able to see to drive home.
23. You need four players for bridge.

Task J pages 92-94

1. a
2. b
3. b
4. a
5. b
6. b
7. a
8. b
9. b
10. a
11. a
12. b
13. a
14. a
15. b
16. a
17. a
18. b
19. a
20. b
21. a
22. b
23. b
24. a
25. a
26. b

Task K pages 95-96

1. went through the gate.
2. oiled them.
3. set her alarm earlier.
4. sat down to rest.
5. took some aspirin.
6. hung up and called her again.
7. took it to the gas station and pumped it up.
8. took his temperature.
9. turned the volume down.
10. put new batteries in the flashlight.
11. sewed it back on with a needle and thread.
12. pushed the alarm button.
13. gave the plants some water.
14. apologize to him.
15. went to the store to buy a prom dress.
16. took another route; followed the detour signs
17. heated it on the stove.
18. went to the library to read it in another copy.
19. opened a bank account.
20. wrote a check.
21. turned the shower off and got the shampoo.
22. called the hostess to find out.
23. brushed the snow off the windshield and the windows before starting to drive.

Task L pages 97-98

1. mix blue and yellow paint; borrow some paint; buy more paint at the store
2. leave it out; substitute honey for the sugar; borrow some from a neighbor; go to the store and buy more sugar
3. split it three ways; put it back in the freezer and not give it to anyone; draw straws to see who gets it; eat it herself
4. use another door; unscrew the legs from the couch; try another angle; buy a new couch
5. put ice on it; cut it out

6. wait at a neighbor's until his wife comes home; try to climb in through an open window; break the glass in the door and unlock it from the inside; call a locksmith

7. tell her friend thanks and don't mention a gift for her; tell her friend that she has her gift but it isn't wrapped yet; tell her the truth, that she hasn't bought her a gift; give the friend a gift that someone else has brought to Jan

8. the children can take turns by hours or by days sitting by the window; the children can draw straws to see who gets to sit by the window; the parents decide who gets to sit where; one of the parents sits in the middle so that there are three windows free.

9. stay home with her daughter and take the day off; call day care and see if they can take her for the day; take the daughter to work with her; ask a neighbor to watch her

10. continue cutting until it begins to rain too hard; stop immediately and wait to cut the other half when the yard dries; go and check the weather forecast to see if it will be raining long

11. hang up and wait for her father-in-law to call her back; obtain a dial tone and try to call her back; call the operator and ask what happened; if the telephone doesn't work, go next door and report the telephone out of order

12. check the fuse to make sure the dryer is heating; take her clothes to the laundromat to dry them; hang her clothes on the line to dry; call a repairman to fix the dryer

13. use barbecue sauce instead; eat the French fries without ketchup; go to the store to buy more ketchup

14. call his dad to bring it; borrow lunch money from the teacher; ask his friends for some of their lunches

15. stop and call her; use a map to find her way; stop at a gas station and ask for directions

16. walk around the stage for a minute until she remembers them; wait for a prompter to whisper them to her; improvise, making up lines to say

17. try to see if the horse stepped on something and remove it; walk back to the stable, leading the horse; tether the horse and go get help

18. go home and change; make a joke over it with her friends; don't mention it, hoping it won't be noticed

19. put on his emergency lights and wait for a policeman or another motorist to stop and help him; walk to the next exit and call for assistance.

20. show the people their ticket stubs and see if they will move; ask them to move; get the manager or usher to take care of it

Task M pages 99-101

1. Use safety pins or tape to hold up the hem.

2. Put the tree in a bucket of sand or put it in a large tin can set inside a cinder block.

3. He could use a belt or an old necktie attached to the dog's collar.

4. Use a small amount of cooking oil or poach the egg instead.

5. Use a long screw driver, an old kitchen spoon, or a clean plant stake.

6. Use two clean washclothes, folded up or use a pair of thick socks folded in half.

7. Use a small amount of glue to hold the paper together or have someone hold the paper shut as you wrap a ribbon very tightly around the package.

8. Ask to use your neighbor's telephone; borrow your neighbor's car or ask for a lift; send your neighbor to your friend's house with your message.

9. She could use a straight pin or a bobby pin or rip the corners and fold them down.

10. Light an oil lamp/lantern, start a fire in the fireplace.

11. Use pipe cleaners twisted around each braid or use ribbon tied very tightly.

12. Turn on the hot water in the shower, close the door and breathe in the steam.

13. Use a razor blade to trim the wispy parts or borrow scissors from your neighbor.

14. Pick up the big pieces; use one piece of paper to rake the pieces onto another and/or use a damp piece of paper towel to pick up the small slivers.

15. Arrange a time when you could be contacted at a relative's or a friend's house; have them contact you by mail.

16. Take a towel and soak it in hot water, wring it out and wrap around the neck.

17. Call or flag down a policeman and ask him to unlock the car for you.

18. Turn around and retrace your steps until you come to something familiar.

19. Call a friend and ask her to call you at 7 A.M.

20. Use his shirt, beach hat, or towel to carry the shells.

21. Use a typewriter or borrow a pencil from a neighbor.

22. Leave a note on the meter to explain to the meter maid.

23. Use a frying pan to cook the hamburgers over the camp fire; make skewers from sticks and roast the hamburgers over the camp fire.

24. Wait until tomorrow and buy a dropcloth when the stores are open; open up the sides of large trash bags to make temporary dropcloths; use newspaper.

25. Screw in a long screw from your toolbox, leaving enough of the tip to pull out with pliers.

26. Use a shovel or a large rock to dig.

27. Use pennies or paper clips to represent the missing red checkers.

Task N pages 102-103

1. a. Go to the pay phone and call her boyfriend.
   b. Ask him to call her mom and give her the message.

2. a. Pick up the plates and napkins.

   b. Place something heavy on them so they don't blow away again.

3. a. Flip a coin to see who gets to watch his show.
   b. The other boy misses his show, tapes it on the VCR, or watches it at a friend's house.

4. a. Look for it outside her house and in her car.
   b. Look for it at work the next day.

5. a. Check in his pockets and in the car for loose change.
   b. Ask the attendant if he can give him what money he has and leave his name and address, paying the rest later.
   c. Come back the next day and pay what he owes.

6. a. Dive in the water and try to find them.
   b. Go to the shore and call someone to bring an extra set.

7. a. Turn off the burner.
   b. Throw away the burnt popcorn.
   c. Pop some more, using a lower temperature and more oil.

8. a. Tim should try on one pair of shoes. If they fit, he should take them home.
   b. If they don't fit, Randy should try them on. If they fit him, he should take them home. If not, Ted should try them on.
   c. The boys should continue in this manner until each boy has a pair of shoes that fit him.

9. a. Turn off the water.
   b. Unplug the drain and let some water out.
   c. Mop the floor.

10. a. Find the leak.
    b. Patch the leak.
    c. Blow up the ball.

11. a. Take the ring off your finger.
    b. Try to pull the ring out of your hair.
    c. If that doesn't work, get scissors and cut it out.

12. a. Check the fuse, breaker switch or the pilot light.
    b. If they are okay, check the oil tank.
    c. If it is full, call the repair company.

13. a. Check the gas level.
    b. Add gas if needed.
    c. Try to start it.
    d. Check for other problems.
    e. Fix them if you can.
    f. Take the mower to a repair shop.

14. a. Stop the machine.
    b. Raise the pressure foot and remove fabric.
    c. Cut upper and lower threads.
    d. Replace needles.
    e. Rethread the machine.
    f. Insert fabric and begin sewing.

15. a. Pull off the road.
    b. Get out the jack, tire iron and spare tire.
    c. Jack up the car.
    d. Take off flat tire.
    e. Put on spare tire.
    f. Lower car to ground.
    g. Put away tools.

16. a. Remove the two-year-old from the tub.
    b. Bundle him in a towel.
    c. Take him with her down the hall to check on the five-year-old.

17. a. Take Laura to the party and drop her off.
    b. Explain that the present was inadvertently left behind.
    c. Immediately get the present and return or bring it when picking up Laura.

18. a. Find a clock in the house to verify the time or call time-of-day.
    b. Stop at a drugstore on her way to the interview to get a new battery for her watch.
    c. Borrow a family member's or friend's watch for the interview if there is not time to purchase the battery.

19. a. Return to the store to make sure the boots are the proper size.
    b. Consult with the clerk as to the appropriate weight sock to wear.
    c. Obtain a refund of the purchase price if the boots continue to be uncomfortable.

20. a. Sarah should get away from the spilled juice to prevent more from dripping on her.
    b. Sarah should ask one of the adults to bring some paper towels or towels to help blot the dress dry.
    c. Sarah should take off her dress to dry if it gets too wet.

21. a. Mr. White should get off the bicycle.
    b. He should put his head down between his knees.
    c. Mr. White should call someone for help if he is still dizzy.

22. a. Look at the newspaper to determine the movies and times.
    b. Call the movie theater to get the prices.

23. a. Marsha should call the airport/train station/bus station, to determine schedules and fares.
    b. Call a friend or family member in the same town as her mother and ask her/him to stay with her mother until Marsha can get there.

24. a. Get the cows out of the road and back in the field.
    b. Locate the place in the fence where they got out.
    c. Repair the fence so they cannot get out again.

25. a. They should swim to the canoe.
    b. They should right the canoe and get back in.

26. a. She should write on looseleaf or pad paper and mail it in a plain envelope.
    b. She should buy more writing paper when she has the opportunity.

Task O pages 104-105

1. The pin will dig in your foot when you put your shoe on.
2. The prescription will be different and you won't be able to see clearly.
3. It might be too much to take at once and could harm you.
4. The chicken will burn on the outside and be raw on the inside.
5. It will foam up and the machine will overflow with suds.
6. The letter will be returned to him for insufficient postage.
7. She will be five cents short.
8. A ruler wouldn't bend as needed to go around the waist.
9. Water will seep through the washcloth and run down the drain.
10. One sleeve will be shorter than the other.
11. Combination locks do not have keys.
12. The liquid cement would run out of the holes in the basket.
13. That will only make it shorter.
14. Oil will be too slippery and he will slide off the board.
15. The fork will break the egg.
16. There is little chance of a doctor walking on a dark country road.
17. The chair would still be lopsided unless all legs were cut down equally.
18. He needs to get some gas first to take care of the primary problem.
19. The next bus may not be going anywhere near where Jean needs to go.
20. This would make the picture lighter and harder to see.

Task P pages 106-109

1. a, b, d
2. b, c
3. a, b, d
4. a b, c, f
5. a, b, d
6. a, b, d, e
7. a, b, d, f
8. a, b, c, e
9. a, b, d, e
10. a, b, d, e
11. a, b, c, d
12. b, d, e
13. a, d, e
14. a, b, c
15. a, b, c, d
16. c, d, e
17. a, b, d
18. a, c, e
19. b, c, d
20. a, b, d, e

21. b, c, d
22. b, c, d, e
23. a, c, d
24. b, c, e

Task Q pages 110-112

1. bought some more when she noticed it was getting low.
2. checked inside the carton before purchasing the eggs.
3. allowed time for the traffic and notified Ned she was going to be late.
4. told his parents of the bad grade and talked about why his performance was poor and how to do better next time.
5. either waited until her nails were dry before calling her friend or she could have used a pencil to dial the numbers.
6. checked to see how much money he had in checking before writing the check.
7. reserved seats for themselves at the theater.
8. notified the post office and have their mail stopped or held during the time they were vacationing.
9. had the repairman give him an estimate on the time it would take to fix the car and made other arrangements for transportation.
10. kept her son home while he was running a temperature or taken him to a doctor.
11. tried the shoes on while she was still at the department store.
12. checked her calendar to see if Friday night was open and gotten back to her neighbor with an answer.
13. been more careful when selecting her luggage and checked the name and baggage numbers.
14. found out his sister's size and asked the clerk for assistance on how the sweaters run. Or he should have bought a non-sale sweater or given her a gift certificate.
15. waited until Monday morning to put the trash out or made sure the lids were on securely.
16. written each appointment on his calendar, and checked his calendar before making any appointments.

17. tried harder to improve her work, or looked earlier for another job.
18. tried the coloring product on a small sample of her hair first.
19. told his aunt the shirt didn't suit his style or didn't fit, so he was going to exchange it.
20. put sunscreen on.
21. been more careful when he last put the game away.

Task R pages 113-132

1. a. Yes, it was a problem because they couldn't get back to shore.
   b. They may have run out of gas or something could be wrong with the motor.
   c. They could row back to shore if they have oars or wait for someone to tow them.
   d. There was no ladder or steps to climb into the boat. She was not strong enough to pull herself up.
   e. She could go to the back of the boat and step on the ledge that holds the motor.
   f. Remain calm and wait for help.
   g. They could swim to shore if they are good swimmers.
   h. They should not try to swim to shore if they aren't good swimmers.

2. a. It wasn't a problem yet but could be in another half hour.
   b. She should wait until 5:30.
   c. She could look for a pay phone or walk to a friend's house.
   d. No one was home. Maybe her mom had an accident or car trouble.
   e. Yes, if she doesn't know her way home or anyone that lives close by.
   f. Go with the neighbor and wait at her house until her mom gets home.
   g. She shouldn't continue to wait on the corner.

3. a. He had locked his keys in the car.
   b. He was busy unloading the clothes and forgot to take the keys out of the ignition.
   c. Ask the cleaners for a coat hanger to unlock the door or call a lock smith. Sometimes the police can help.
   d. He forgot to put on the emergency brake.
   e. He needs to get into his car.
   f. Answers will vary.
   g. Answers will vary.

4. a. Their food had been eaten and they had no way to notify someone to help them.
   b. They got wet.
   c. They couldn't be used until they dried out, so the boys couldn't build a fire.
   d. They could make camp and eat what little food they had left. They could go down the mountain. They could look for other campers to help them. They could send up flares for help if they have any.
   e. They shouldn't start down the mountain if they don't know the way.

5. a. The calls interrupt her and frighten her. She wants them to stop now but will have to wait a month.
   b. She needs to leave the phone on the hook because of her mother's help.
   c. Betsy could get an answering machine. She could take the phone off the hook and have friends and mom call a neighbor if they need her. She could get a whistle to blow into the receiver if the caller is listening.
   d. She should not disconnect her phone without telling people how to reach her.

6. a. He had no money for the weekend.
   b. He could go to the bank on Saturday morning. He could write checks or use credit cards. He could borrow from a friend.
   c. He still needed money for the weekend.
   d. Use credit cards, write checks, or borrow from a friend.
   e. Mug somebody or rob a bank.
   f. He could have gone to the bank on Thursday or Friday during his lunch hour. His business could direct deposit his check.

7. a. Matt picked up the wrong books and notebooks. He cannot do his homework without his books. His friend cannot do her homework without her books. It is evening and school is closed.
   b. He was busy talking with his friend and wasn't paying attention to the books.
   c. Matt can't do his homework because he doesn't have his own books.
   d. He doesn't have his own books. He should call a friend to see if they can study together. He should call his friend to see if she picked up his books by mistake. He should call the janitor to see if he can get into school to see if his books are still there.
   e. He should not forget to do his homework. He should not put the books back where he picked them up.

8. a. It wasn't a problem yet but could be if she continues riding.
   b. She could decide to go home. She could look for signs of a store or shop where she could buy something to eat.
   c. Carol was hungry. She was lost. It was getting cold and beginning to get dark.
   d. She is lost and does not know which trail to take home. She is cold and hungry. She could be in danger.
   e. She could stop for the night and camp. She could send a signal to others.
   f. She should not continue riding on unfamiliar trails after dark.

9. a. It was a problem because Val is to go to a party for Barb on Friday night.
   b. Val could tell Barb she has plans that evening. She could make plans to go to a movie with Val another time.
   c. She was caught offguard.
   d. Make sure that Barb shows up at the party so she can enjoy the surprise.
   e. Val should change her plans with Barb. She should insist on driving and take Barb to the surprise party instead of the movie. Val should move the party to her house.
   f. She should not tell Barb about the party. She should not go to the movie and miss the party.

10. a. Larry was cold. The room was full of smoke. Larry could be overcome by smoke.
    b. The logs were too wet. The flue in the fireplace was not open.
    c. He could make sure the flue was open. He could get a wet cloth to put over his mouth to help him breathe.
    d. The smoke may be harmful to Larry.
    e. He should open the windows and vents. He should leave the room.
    f. He should not let the smoke alarm go off or call the fire department unless someone or something is in danger.

11. a. Mike was ill. He has missed three days of work. He may not have accrued any sick leave and may not be paid for the days he missed work.
    b. Mike may have made a poor impression on his new employers.
    c. He has missed three days of work.
    d. He should get a note from his doctor about his illness. He should offer to make up some time by working in the evening or weekend when he is not ill. He should check with personnel about accrued sickleave.

191

e. He should not demand to be paid for sick leave until he has checked on company policy. He should not take additional time off work in the near future. He should not go to work while ill if it would be harmful to himself or others.

12. a. April needs one more invitation and has run out of them.
b. She could go to the store and buy more. She could use a different kind of invitation. She could make an invitation.
c. It wasn't a problem because April could use a different kind of invitation.
d. She wanted the invitations to reflect the "clown" theme.
e. She wanted to find the same kind of invitation.
f. The child who has not yet been invited should receive an invitation.
g. April should send the child an invitation or call his parents to invite him to the party.
h. She should not forget to invite the child to the party.

13. a. The class has too many students in it.
b. Diane needs the class in order to graduate. There are too many students who want to take the class.
c. Diane has been dropped from the class and will not graduate this semester.
d. She should talk with the professor to see if she can attend the class with special permission.
e. She should not decide to take the class later if she wants to graduate this semester.

14. a. Boston was having bad weather.
b. It was a problem because he wanted to fly to Boston to attend his brother's wedding.
c. He could wait for the next flight to Boston. He could drive or take a train.
d. The weather was bad.

e. He might be late for the wedding.
f. He should call his brother and discuss the problem. He should consider driving to Boston.
g. He should drive with the others. He should find out about weather conditions and consider waiting for a plane.
h. He should not miss the wedding.

15. a. It was a problem because the walls of the kitchen would not match.
b. She could go back to the store and get another roll of paper.
c. The wallpaper did not match. The store was about to close. There were no rolls of matching paper available at the store.
d. Deena needs another roll of matching wallpaper.
e. She should call other stores the next day to find out if they have the wallpaper she needs.
f. She shouldn't leave one section of the kitchen without wallpaper. She shouldn't rip the wallpaper she has hung off the wall.

16. a. Andrew was playing unsupervised. He put things in the toilet that did not belong there.
b. His mother could have supervised him.
c. The toilet overflowed. The floor and carpet were wet.
d. Andrew put things in the toilet and flushed it.
e. He fell and possibly hurt himself.
f. Andrew was not being supervised. He might get hurt.
g. She should supervise him. She should give him something to do. She should keep the bathroom door closed. She should call a plumber.
h. She shouldn't punish Andrew. She shouldn't leave him unsupervised.

17. a. Rosemarie had no checks to use to pay for her groceries.
b. She forgot to get some at the bank.
c. She could use cash or a credit card instead.
d. Rosemarie had no checks or cash to pay for the groceries. She cannot take the groceries home.
e. She needed to pay for the items sold to her.
f. She should ask the cashier to keep the groceries while she goes to the bank.
g. She shouldn't decide to get groceries another day and leave those with the cashier.

18. a. Gary was hungry and tired. The brakes failed.
b. The mountain was steep and there were many curves.
c. They were overheated.
d. Gary should use the emergency brake.
e. Gary is in danger of hurting himself and others.
f. Gary should stay in his lane of traffic. He should shift to a lower gear. He should drive on the grass to slow the speed of the car.
g. He shouldn't jump from the car or turn it off.

19. a. The car was sliding down the hill.
b. It was snowing and the street was slick.
c. Harold should steer the car, shift to a lower gear, and set the emergency brake.
d. He should not slam on the brakes because the car will spin on the slippery road.
e. He caught his pant leg on the seat lever.
f. He could reach down with his hand and free his pant leg. He could rip his pants to free his leg.
g. Stop the car before Harold gets hit or goes over the ravine.
h. He shouldn't put on the brake without pressing in the clutch since the car will stall and he will have no control.

i. He could steer the car toward the shoulder of the road, hoping it will stop when it reaches the bottom of the hill.

20. a. The movers couldn't get the box springs into the attic stairwell.
b. Gretchen could sell it to a friend or place a sale advertisement in the newspaper.
c. They could remove the springs from the wooden slats of the box springs and reassemble it once upstairs in the attic.
d. They should not try to force the box springs through the narrow turn. Gretchen should not throw it away.
e. Gretchen can't use the new box springs and mattress in the attic because they are too large.
f. She should put them in another room for the overnight guests. She could use the bedding she just bought in her room and move another mattress and box springs into the attic.
g. She should not yell at the movers because it doesn't fit. She should not give it away.

Social Language

Tasks A through E

Accept reasonable answers.

Task D   pages 150-152

1. a
2. b
3. a
4. b
5. b
6. a
7. a
8. b
9. b
10. a
11. b
12. a
13. b
14. a
15. b
16. b
17. b
18. a
19. a
20. b
21. a
22. a
23. b
24. a

25. b
26. a
27. a

Task E page 153

1. I refuse to go.
   I'll go another day.
   Someone else may go.
2. Are we really having pizza?
   Are you sure we're having it for dinner?
   And you aren't having pizza for dinner?
3. And not eight or ten.
   I had a feeling you'd be here then.
   Someone else came at nine.
4. I'm too old for a doll or I'm undeserving.
   What a great/awful gift!
   I didn't expect you to do it.
5. He didn't notice me.
   And not by you.
   He wasn't running.
6. No one was absent.
   No one was anywhere else but the gym.
   They were at the gym but they're gone now.
7. Not all of them.
   But not the other foods.
   Can you believe it?
8. He's not absolutely sure.
   But no one else does.
   He's kidding himself!
9. None should be allowed.
   But they can be allowed outside it.
   That rule just makes sense.
10. Are you being truthful?
    I can't believe it.
    I believe it, but do you?
11. But other people get help.
    I don't get help from anybody.
    But they do other things to me.
12. Not her first name.
    I'm telling the truth.
    But not his.

Task F page 154

1. starts
2. starts, finishes
3. starts
4. maintains
5. finishes
6. starts
7. maintains
8. maintains
9. maintains
10. finishes
11. starts
12. finishes
13. maintains, finishes
14. starts
15. maintains
16. starts
17. starts, finishes
18. finishes
19. starts
20. finishes
21. maintains
22. starts
23. starts, maintains
24. finishes

Task G pages 155-156

1. What school did you go to before you came here?
2. Nice day, isn't it?
3. What's your name?
4. Could you please help me?
5. How are you, Grandmother?
6. Will you take my order, please?
7. Thanks for the mail.
8. Hello, my name is Beth Williams.
9. Can you help me, please?
10. Happy Birthday!
11. How was your trip?
12. I'm having trouble with the picture on my TV.
13. Welcome home!
14. My name is Brown and I have a reservation.
15. Do you work in this building?
16. Can you help me, please?
17. Do you have insurance?
18. Nice party, isn't it?
19. Was I speeding, officer?
20. Have you seen this movie?
21. May I help you?
22. Congratulations on your new baby.
23. I'm sorry. I'll replace it for you.
24. Susan hasn't been feeling well.

Task H

Accept reasonable answers.

Task I pages 160-162

1. Stop! There's a car coming!
2. No, get down!
3. May I have your other candy bar?
4. May I please have my softball?
5. Will you please move your car so I can back out?
6. I'm here to pick up my photographs. My name is Jones.
7. How much longer will I have to wait?
8. Hello, my name is _____.
9. Would you be able to help me with the parade on Saturday?
10. I made the reservation a week ago. Please check again.

11. Look out! Here comes a car!
12. Excuse me. I believe I'm next.
13. I can't talk right now. I'm busy.
14. Everyone take your seat. It's time for math.
15. May I have the check please?
16. Encore!
17. I'm feeling sick. Can we stop the car?
18. May I help you?
19. All aboard!
20. Look out for falling rocks!
21. Please don't talk while the movie is playing.
22. May I see your license, please?
23. Rider behind you, passing to the left!
24. Can you feel this?

Task J pages 163-165

1. I'm glad you can come! See you on Saturday.
2. Thanks, anyway!
3. Thanks, so did you!
4. Sure, I'll bring it over.
5. Sure, I'd be happy to.
6. Congratulations!
7. That's okay.
8. Bye, have a good trip!
9. That's okay, maybe you'll remember tomorrow.
10. Thanks, I like it!
11. I'm sorry. We're glad to have you back!
12. Thanks for having us.
13. Thanks for checking.
14. I'm sorry. Hope it was a happy one!
15. Thanks, I like my job.
16. I'm sorry. I know how much you liked it.
17. I'm sorry to hear about your dad.
18. Sure, I'd love to!
19. Maybe I could spend the night another time.
20. I'm glad no one was hurt.
21. I need to cut down on sweets.
22. No, thank you.
23. Thanks, I'd like to visit soon.
24. I'm sorry the car was hit.
25. I'm glad you're here now.
26. Thanks for coming to visit.
27. I'm sorry, but you'll have to go to bed now.

Task K

Accept reasonable answers.

Task L pages 169-170

1. The milk would stay in the bowl.
2. There would be no lead to make the mark.

3. The shovel wouldn't be sharp enough.
4. The tape wouldn't hold the wallpaper up.
5. There is no water in the desert.
6. There is no wind in the house and not enough room.
7. The car couldn't move.
8. The mail carrier won't deliver mail without a stamp.
9. You eat the inside of the egg, not the shell.
10. There wouldn't be enough room.
11. It would be too hard to run.
12. A television won't run without electricity.
13. A dog isn't smart enough to do homework.
14. They wouldn't fit.
15. They would melt.
16. The sun isn't hot enough.
17. It's against the law; someone might get hurt.
18. Only parents can adopt.
19. You would fall down!
20. You need to be able to use two arms to climb a tree.
21. You can't chew the kernels well.
22. You have to cut the outside to get to the inside.
23. Phone numbers are listed by last names.
24. Seventy-five is an odd number and would not divide evenly between two people.

Task M pages 171-172

1. They will melt.
2. It will spoil.
3. You might get sick.
4. You might bump your head on the bottom of the pool.
5. You might catch the cold.
6. Someone might trip over them.
7. It could be stolen.
8. Someone might steal it.
9. They could die from too much water.
10. It might be too hot.
11. It could blow away.
12. It will run out of the bottle and spill.
13. You might get dog hairs on your shirt.
14. You wouldn't be able to see.
15. Someone might steal it.
16. It will make a spot on the table.
17. It will clog the drain.
18. You could get hit by a car.
19. You might hurt your eyes.

20. Gasoline will explode and start a fire.
21. You might get a shock.
22. You might fall in the water and drown.
23. You could get electrocuted.
24. He might want to rob you.
25. He might go into the street.

Task N   pages 173-174

1. No, my name is not Smith, it's Wilson.
2. No, I live in the United States, not Russia.
3. No, Christmas comes in December, not in March.
4. No, you cook toast in a toaster, not in a refrigerator.
5. No, an adult drives a car, not a baby.
6. No, John is a boy's name, not a girl's name.
7. No, you use a rake to rake leaves, not a broom.
8. No, people put on their coats when it is cold, not their shorts.
9. No, you heat a tea bag in hot water to make tea, not in the oven.
10. No, you wash laundry in a washing machine, not in a furnace.
11. No, a mail carrier helps you send a letter, not a long-distance operator.
12. No, you wear earmuffs on your ears to keep warm, not mittens.
13. No, I sleep at night, not during the day.
14. No, you eat sandwiches for lunch, not nails.
15. No, I wear a hat on my head, not a boot.
16. No, a bathtub is used for bathing, not swimming.
17. No, I eat apples and cheese for snacks, not bugs.
18. No, birds live in trees, not dogs.
19. No, I purchase things with money, not buttons.
20. No, glasses help you see better, not hear better.
21. No, a flagpole is used to hang a flag, not to sleep on.
22. No, I wear clothes when going outside, not when taking a bath.
23. No, a waiter takes your order in a restaurant, not a doctor.
24. No, animals live at the zoo, not children.

Task O   pages 175-176

1. Penguins can't fly.
2. My principal is five feet, six inches tall.
3. My doctor doesn't have a driver's license.
4. My friend didn't tell me she was giving me a surprise party.
5. I drink orange juice every day and had the flu last week.
6. My friend is an actor and he can't sing or dance.
7. The Fourth of July was last Monday.
8. Last fall there was a hurricane named Bill.
9. Factory smoke also pollutes the air.
10. We have a flag in our yard and we aren't government officials.
11. The Mississippi River empties into the Gulf of Mexico.
12. Minneapolis is the largest city in Minnesota, but St. Paul is the capital.
13. Sandra Day O'Conner is a female Supreme Court justice.
14. Immigrants to the U.S. must live here five years before they can become citizens.
15. Some accidents have been caused by the weather or mechanical failure.
16. Some music written after 1962 is called "New Wave."
17. The winter Olympics was held in Canada in 1988.
18. My two-door car was made in the U.S.
19. I listed just my last name and first initial.
20. The show I saw last night at 8:00 P.M. was violent.
21. My uncle entered the university when he was 15 years old.
22. Our city of 250,000 doesn't have mass transit.
23. Thomas Jefferson was also a farmer.
24. Some people run as Independent candidates without a party.

Tasks P and Q

Accept reasonable answers.